DAVID FICKLING BOOKS AND THE PHO

PHILIP PULLMAN

THE ADVENTURES OF JOHN BLAKE

MYSTERY OF THE GHOST SHIP

M

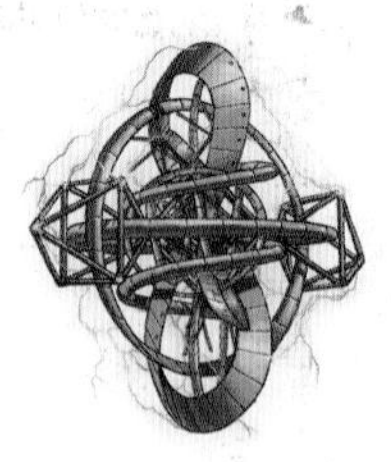

To the spirit of *The Phoenix* – P. P.

For Goosey. With special thanks to Camille – F. F.

THE ADVENTURES OF JOHN BLAKE
MYSTERY OF THE GHOST SHIP

is a

CO-PRODUCTION BETWEEN
DAVID FICKLING BOOKS AND THE PHOENIX COMIC

First published in hardback in Great Britain in 2017 by
David Fickling Books and The Phoenix Comic

www.davidficklingbooks.com
www.thephoenixcomic.co.uk

This paperback edition published 2018

978-1-78845-059-1

1 3 5 7 9 10 8 6 4 2

WARNING: This book will give you a thirst for adventure!

Papers used by David Fickling Books are from responsible sources.

DAVID FICKLING BOOKS Reg. No. 8340307

A CIP catalogue record for this book is available from the British Library.

Printed and bound in China by Toppan Leefung

Edited by Alice Corrie and Tom Fickling
Designed by Becky Chilcott

YOU SEEN IT YET?

JEEZ, BOSUN!
SHUT UP. LISTEN...
THIS AIN'T A NORMAL FOG.
NO, IT AIN'T.
HEY, BOSUN –
WHAT THE HELL ARE YOU DOING WITH THAT GUN?
THIS AIN'T PIRATES.
DON'T LOOK IN HIS EYES.
WHAT EYES? WHOSE EYES?
YOU MUSTN'T LOOK IN HIS EYES, WHATEVER YOU DO.
WHY?
WHO?
WHAT YOU TALKING ABOUT? WHAT EYES?
THEY SAY YOU BE DEAD IN A MONTH IF YOU LOOK IN HIS EYES!

I DON'T WANT TO HEAR NO MORE 'BOUT IT.
I DON'T BLAME YOU.
WHAT'S THAT?
IT'S A SHIP.
PORT QUARTER! ON THE PORT QUARTER!
OKING
GOT IT, SIR! ABOUT A HUNDRED METRES...

BIP..
BIP...
DOUSE THE LIGHTS.
AYE, AYE, SIR.
SIXTY METRES, SIR...
FIFTY...
FORTY...
WAIT!
WAIT...
KRAK!
KRAK!
STOW THAT!
IT'S GOING TO CRASH!

OH, MOTHER OF GOD PROTECT US...

YOU SEE HIS FACE? HUH?
NO.
NO. I DIDN'T LOOK.
IT'S GONE! IT'S JUST...
IT'S NOT THERE ...
YOU LUCKY.
YOU LOOK IN HIS EYES, YOU BE DEAD IN A MONTH.

International Marine Organization, San Francisco_

DANIELLE,
SCHWARTZ WANTS TO SEE YOU. HE SAYS YOUR PHONE'S OUT OF ORDER.

THAT'S THE INTENTION.

BUT LOOK, CHRIS, THE *MARY ALICE* – ANOTHER SIGHTING! A TANKER OFF SOMALIA.
THAT'S FOUR THIS YEAR.

EVERY OCEAN IN THE WORLD, AND ALWAYS THE SAME STORY: THERE'S A FOG - SHE TURNS UP - THE FOG CLEARS - SHE'S GONE!
THE TANKER CREW WAS EXPECTING PIRATES, SO THEY HAD RIFLES.
THEY NEVER HEARD OF CAMERAS, THESE PEOPLE?
I THINK MAYBE THIS IS WHAT SCHWARTZ WANTED TO SEE YOU ABOUT.
... THAT'S WHY I PULLED THE PLUG ON THE PHONE. HE'S ONLY GOING TO TELL ME TO STOP.
HAVE YOU COPIED EVERYTHING?
ER, EVERYTHING EXCEPT WHAT SHE'S JUST PUT UP.
YOU HAVE HER ADDRESS, RIGHT?
I... UH... SURE MR HARLAND ...
LET HER CARRY ON, AND GET ME HER ADDRESS.
CAM 1
YOU GOT THIS ALL BACKED UP, RIGHT?
YEAH, AND HARD COPIES. I'M NOT STUPID, CHRIS.
WELL MAKE SURE YOU KEEP THEM SAFE. AND KEEP ME IN THE LOOP. I LOVE THIS STUFF.
DON'T WORRY, IT'S NOT LIKE SCHWARTZ IS GOING TO SEARCH MY APARTMENT IS IT?
HER ADDRESS.
NOW.

Blackfriars Bridge, London_

!
DOFF

HNNGK
?!
EVENING, GENTLEMEN.

LET'S KEEP THIS SIMPLE. I GET THE CASE. YOU KEEP YOUR DIGNITY.
DEAL?

BANG

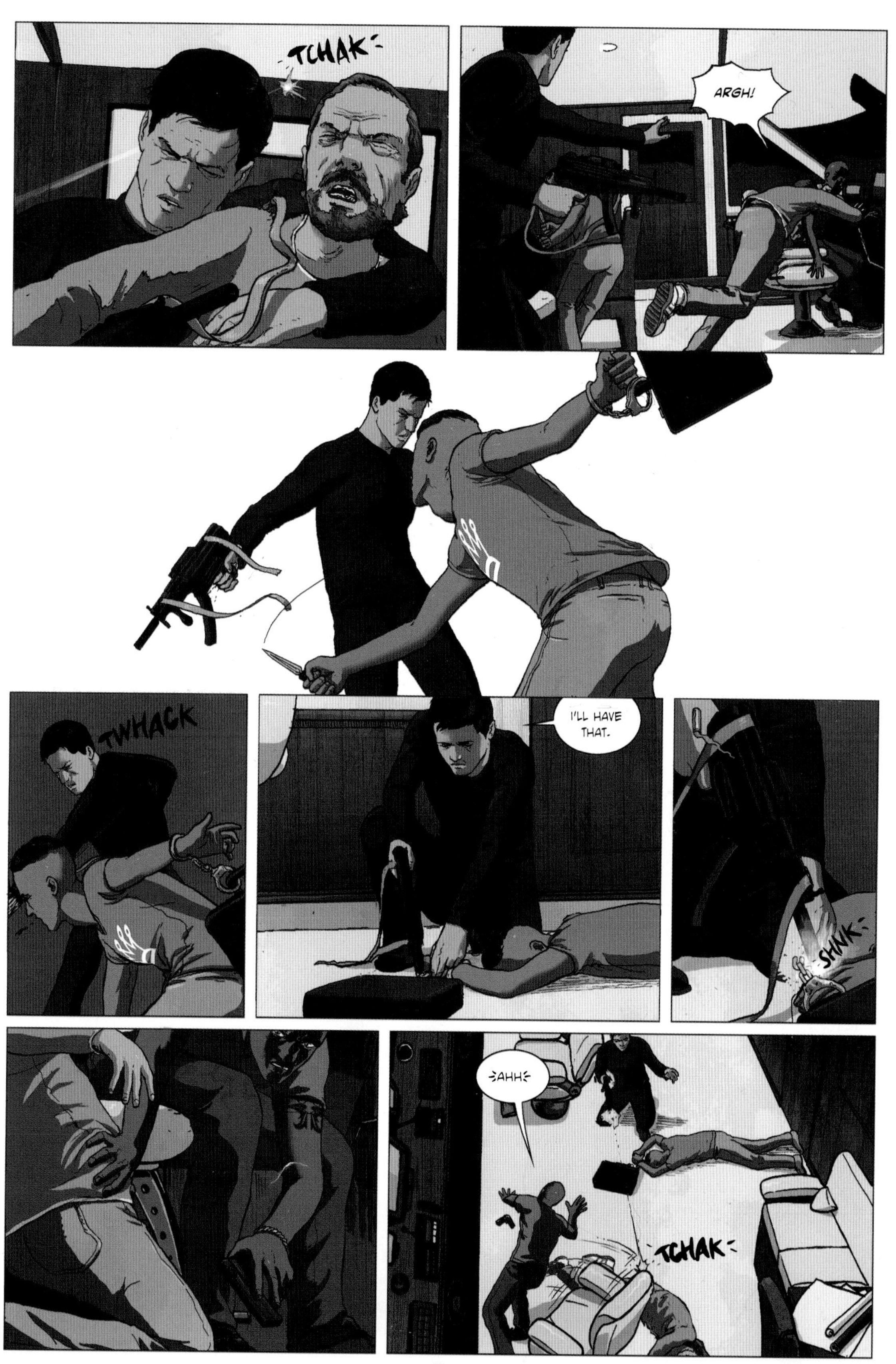
TCHAK
ARGH!
TWHACK
I'LL HAVE THAT.
SHNK
AHH
TCHAK

BETTER GET BACK TO THE WHEEL. TOWER BRIDGE JUST AHEAD.
DON'T DAMAGE IT.
DO YOU HAVE ANY IDEA WHOSE BOAT THIS IS?!
HEY!
THERE YOU ARE! WHAT'S WRONG WITH YOUR RADIO? REPORT TO THE BRIDGE IMMEDIATELY!
OH, BUT WHAT – OH. OK SIR, I WAS JUST...
?
HEY! WAIT! YOU, COME BACK! WHO ARE YOU?
TCHAK

SSCCCCRRRRRREEEEEEE

EVENING, SIR. BUSY NIGHT?
NO, NO, VERY QUIET, HANCOCK.
GO STRAIGHT ON IN. THEY'RE EXPECTING YOU.
ROGER – GOOD SHOW. GOT SOMETHING FOR US?

EVENING, MA'AM. HELLO, TOM.
NOTHING IN HERE THAT'LL GO BANG, I HOPE?
SCAN SAYS IT WAS CLEAR, BUT I'D CROSS MY FINGERS IF I WERE YOU.
ANY PROBLEMS?
THEY MADE A BIT OF A DENT IN TOWER BRIDGE.
IT'LL SURVIVE. HAVE A DRINK.
LOOKS LIKE WE WERE RIGHT.
HM...
PENTAGRAM FOUNDATION
WHAT'S THE PENTAGRAM FOUNDATION?
A DODGY ORGANISATION WITH VERY SHADOWY OWNERS.
WHAT DOES IT DO?
WE'RE NOT SURE. BUT THIS IS HENRY HARLAND, KNOWN PENTAGRAM ASSOCIATE AND EXPERT ON ENHANCED INTERROGATION TECHNIQUES.
YOU MEAN TORTURE?
THAT'S THE ENGLISH WORD, YES.
SO HOW DOES THIS HARLAND KNOW ABOUT THE *MARY ALICE*?
PROBABLY THE SAME WAY WE DO. AND THAT'S WHAT WORRIES ME.
BUT HARLAND'S JUST AN ATTACK DOG. AND EVERY DOG HAS A MASTER.
WE JUST NEED TO FIND HIM.
OR HER.

I'LL RUN SOME SEARCHES, SEE IF WE CAN FOLLOW THE TRAIL A LITTLE FURTHER DOWN THE PATH.
THANK YOU, TOM.
LET'S MOVE ON, ROGER. UPDATE ME ON WHERE YOU ARE WITH THE CYCLONE BUSINESS.
IT WASN'T AN OFFICIAL OPERATION, BUT A TOP SECRET PROJECT, AN EXPERIMENT AT SEA THAT WENT WRONG.
IT WAS A WEAPONS BUSINESS: SOMETHING TO DO WITH HIGH-ENERGY PARTICLES.
THEY HITCHED A RIDE WITH THE EINSTEIN-CARMICHAEL EXPEDITION AND NO ONE WOULD EVER SPEAK ABOUT IT AFTERWARDS.
THE SCHOONER WAS INVOLVED SOMEHOW, THE SO-CALLED GHOST SHIP, THE *MARY ALICE*, BUT... THAT'S ALL WE KNOW.
HER MAJESTY'S GOVERNMENT IS VERY KEEN TO FIND THE *MARY ALICE* BEFORE THE OTHER INTERESTED PARTIES. TIME IS NOT ON OUR SIDE.
THERE'S A MEMBER OF MY CLUB IT MIGHT BE WORTH YOU TALKING TO.
PROFESSOR HOLT...
AN ORIGINAL MEMBER OF THE EXPEDITION.
HE MUST BE A HUNDRED YEARS OLD!
EVEN OLDER, ACTUALLY.
DON'T WASTE ANY TIME.
HAS ANYONE ELSE SPOKEN TO HIM?
A LONG TIME AGO, BUT THEY WEREN'T LOOKING FOR WHAT YOU ARE.
THANK YOU, MA'AM.

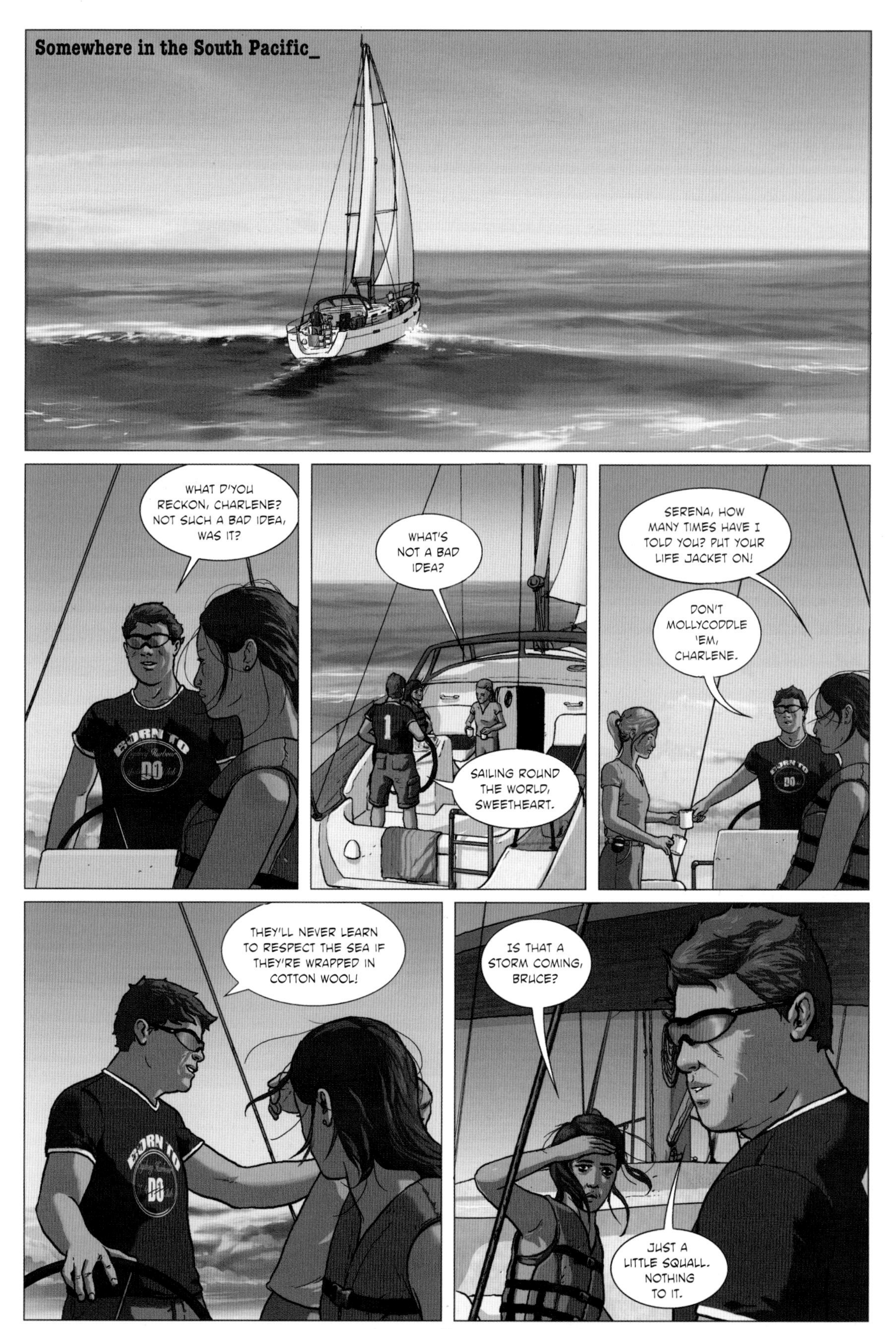
Somewhere in the South Pacific_
WHAT D'YOU RECKON, CHARLENE? NOT SUCH A BAD IDEA, WAS IT?
WHAT'S NOT A BAD IDEA?
SAILING ROUND THE WORLD, SWEETHEART.
SERENA, HOW MANY TIMES HAVE I TOLD YOU? PUT YOUR LIFE JACKET ON!
DON'T MOLLYCODDLE 'EM, CHARLENE.
THEY'LL NEVER LEARN TO RESPECT THE SEA IF THEY'RE WRAPPED IN COTTON WOOL!
IS THAT A STORM COMING, BRUCE?
JUST A LITTLE SQUALL. NOTHING TO IT.

THAT LOOKS LIKE A STORM ...
DAD'LL KNOW WHAT TO DO.

YOU RECKON?
TAP TAP

WHOA

YOU, KIDS! LIFE JACKETS – *NOW!*
JUST A MINUTE – I NEED ROY TO LOWER THE SAIL – THE DAMN THING'S STUCK AGAIN.

ROY! ROY! THE GENNY – PULL ON THAT SHEET.
BRUCE, HE HAS TO HAVE A LIFE JACKET!
ROY! WAKE UP, YOU MONGREL!
BORN TO
DO

WHAT'S HE MEAN? I CAN'T HEAR.
THE WINCH IS PLAYING UP.

C'MON! GET DOWN YOU BLOODY –
CLAK
WHAT THE HELL'S THE MATTER WITH THE DAMN THING?
KIDS! CLIP YOUR LIFELINES ON! RIGHT NOW!
THE SAIL –
DAMN THE SAIL!
ROY – SERENA –
BRRRBBBRRRRRROOMMMMMNNN
BLLLMMNNNNNNNBBBLLLMN

KRAK!
SNAP
ROY! WHAT THE HELL HAVE YOU DONE, YOU MORON?
BORN TO
ROY! SERENA!
ARE YOU...
SERENA!
OH GOD –
I TRIED TO HOLD ON TO HER, MUM – BUT SHE SLIPPED OUT OF MY HAND –

BRUCE! SERENA'S GONE – SHE'S OVERBOARD – TURN THE BOAT AROUND, FOR GOD'S SAKE!
ARE YOU CRAZY? HOW CAN I TURN HER ROUND IN A STORM LIKE THIS?
IF THAT BLOODY BOY HADN'T...
IT'S NOT ROY'S FAULT! DON'T YOU UNDERSTAND? SERENA'S GONE!
HELP! HELP ME! MUM!
URGH... BRUGH... HELP... GURGH!

BRUCE! FOR GOD'S SAKE – THE ENGINE! NEVER MIND THE DAMN SAILS...
THE INSTRUMENTS HAVE GONE CRAZY – WHERE'S THIS FOG COME FROM?
SNAP!
MUM –
DAD –
HELP ME – HELP –
SERENA!
WHAT'S THAT?

BRUCE! MIND OUT –
IT'S GOING TO CRASH INTO US!
WHAT THE...
WHAT THE HELL WAS THAT FOOL DOING?
SERENA!
SERENA!

WHO –
WHAT –
DON'T
STRUGGLE!
Mary A

Mary Alice
HK
PTOU
THAT'S IT – SIT UP.
WHERE? WHO?
DON'T TALK. JUST GET WARM.

NAM PUELLA EST?
THAT'S NOT A GIRL, IS IT?
VERO. PUELLA.
YES, A GIRL.
CAP'N QUAYLE! WE GOT A PASSENGER!
WHO'S THIS, THEN?
SERENA HENDERSON, SIR.
WHAT YEAR IS IT WHERE YOU COME FROM?
WHAT... WHAT?
I SAID WHAT YEAR IS IT? WHAT'S THE DATE?
WELL, IT'S 2017...
TWO THOUSAND AND SEVENTEEN ... DOESN'T TIME FLY?
TAKE OUR PASSENGER TO THE FIRST CLASS SALOON. SPARE NO LUXURY, GENTLEMEN.

AND YOU, BLAKE, NEXT TIME YOU WANT TO BE A HERO, TRY AND FISH UP AN ABLE SEAMAN.
MERRIFIELD! STEER TWO POINTS WEST!
AYE, SIR! TWO POINTS WEST!
GET THAT MAINSAIL IN, AND BE QUICK ABOUT IT.
Mary Alic
WHO...
WHO ARE YOU?
I'M JOHN.
WELCOME ABOARD.

1929?
YOU'RE TRYING TO SAIL TO 1929?
THE YEAR?
WELL, NOT ALL OF US WANT TO GO TO 1929, BUT THAT'S WHERE WE'RE HEADED FIRST.
WHAT, UH...?
WHAT DOES THAT MEAN?

WE A GHOST SHIP. YOU SAIL WITH US, YOU DOOMED. NEVER MIND. EAT SOUP FIRST, DIE LATER.
HUH?
THANKS...
YES, YOU BET, WE A GHOST SHIP, NO WORRIES. WE ALL DEAD MEN.
IS THERE... HAVE YOU GOT A RADIO? I NEED TO LET MY PARENTS KNOW I'M SAFE...
HAH!
YOU WANT A RADIO? WHAT, YOU WANT A ORCHESTRA TOO?
YOU'RE IN A PICKLE, MISS. YOU'RE IN A WORSE SITUATION THAN YOU COULD EVER IMAGINE.
YOU MIGHTA DONE BETTER TO STAY UNDERWATER.
?
WAIT! YOU CAN'T JUST –
HEY!
UH...
AHEM
...

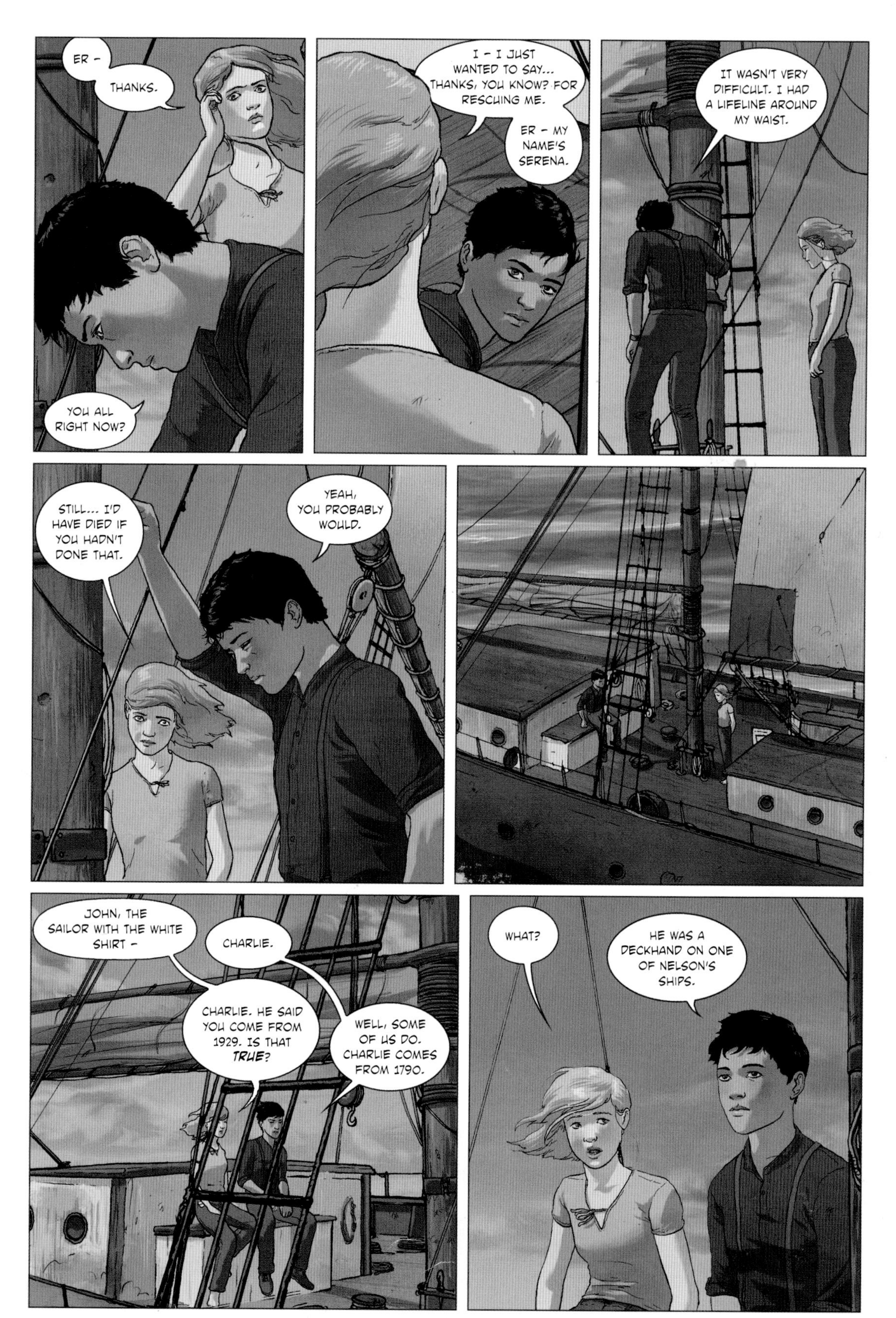
ER –
THANKS.
YOU ALL RIGHT NOW?
I – I JUST WANTED TO SAY... THANKS, YOU KNOW? FOR RESCUING ME.
ER – MY NAME'S SERENA.
IT WASN'T VERY DIFFICULT. I HAD A LIFELINE AROUND MY WAIST.
STILL... I'D HAVE DIED IF YOU HADN'T DONE THAT.
YEAH, YOU PROBABLY WOULD.
JOHN, THE SAILOR WITH THE WHITE SHIRT –
CHARLIE.
CHARLIE. HE SAID YOU COME FROM 1929. IS THAT *TRUE*?
WELL, SOME OF US DO. CHARLIE COMES FROM 1790.
WHAT?
HE WAS A DECKHAND ON ONE OF NELSON'S SHIPS.

SAMMY...
WE PICKED UP SAMMY IN 1913 FROM A JUNK WRECKED IN THE SOUTH CHINA SEA.
DICK MERRIFIELD WAS A SLAVE OF THE BARBARY PIRATES. IT WAS 1614 WHEN WE RESCUED HIM.
AND THERE'S MARCUS TULLIUS PALLAS. IT WAS ABOUT THE YEAR 210 WHEN HE JOINED US. HARD TO TELL, THOUGH. NO NEWSPAPERS IN THOSE DAYS.
AN ANCIENT ROMAN?
HE'S THE ENGINEER.
YEAH, RIGHT.
HE TOOK TO DIESEL ENGINES LIKE A DUCK TO WATER. THE ROMANS WERE GREAT ENGINEERS.
?
WELL... WHEN ARE WE NOW? ARE WE IN MY NOW, OR YOURS?
WE DON'T KNOW WHEN THIS IS. BESIDES THE YEARS I MENTIONED WE'VE BEEN TO 1936, 1634, 1512, 1768, 1493, AND DOZENS MORE...
...
WAIT! I CAN CALL MY PARENTS!
WHAT'S THAT?
IT'S AN APPARATOR.

WHAT DOES IT DO?
EVERYTHING, MORE OR LESS...
TAP TAP
IS IT BROKEN?
NO. THAT'S NIRVANA.
WHAT'S THE CD STAND FOR?
THAT'S THE LOGO OF THE DAHLBERG CORPORATION.
THE WHAT?
THE COMPANY THAT MAKES IT. THE GUY WHO INVENTED IT IS CALLED CARLOS DAHLBERG.
NOTHING'S HAPPENING ... NO SIGNAL AT ALL. THE WHOLE WORLD'S GONE QUIET.

Ealing, West London_
YES?
GOOD MORNING. I TELEPHONED EARLIER. I'M COMMANDER –
OH YES – FROM THE ADMIRALTY. MY FATHER'S IN HIS WORKSHOP.
PLEASE DON'T TIRE HIM OUT.
HE'S VERY FRAIL.
I HAVE TO BE STERN WITH VISITORS, I'M AFRAID.
OH, AND IF YOU HAVE ANY DEVICES ON YOU, I'LL HAVE TO TAKE THEM.
MY FATHER CAN'T STAND THE THINGS.
THAT ALL?
YES.

YES?
IT'S OPEN.
WHAT D'YE WANT?
WHO ARE YOU?
OH YES - ADMIRALTY. COME IN.
THANKS FOR GIVING ME YOUR TIME, PROFESSOR ...
NOT MY TIME TO GIVE. TIME DOESN'T WORK LIKE THAT. SIT DOWN.
TELL ME WHAT YOU WANT.
I BELIEVE YOU WERE A MEMBER OF THE 1929 EINSTEIN-CARMICHAEL EXPEDITION.
WELL?
THERE WAS A SCIENTIST CALLED BLAKE IN THE PARTY.
THAT'S RIGHT.
WHAT WAS HE INVESTIGATING?
HE DIDN'T TALK MUCH. WAS ONLY INTERESTED IN THE EXPERIMENT. AND HIS SON. JAMES, WAS IT?
NO, JOHN. VERY BRIGHT BOY...
YOU KNOW THE FAMOUS DEMONSTRATION OF EINSTEIN'S THEORY IN THE ECLIPSE OF 1919?
WELL, SOME OF THE OBSERVATIONS WERE CURIOUS.
QUESTIONS UNANSWERED.
HENCE THE VOYAGE YOU'RE SO INTERESTED IN.

BLAKE'S EXPERIMENT WAS A MYSTERY TO MOST OF US. FUNDED BY THE WAR OFFICE. HE WAS PLANNING TO USE GRAVITATIONAL ENERGY TO DISTORT TIME ITSELF...
HE DID EXPLAIN IT TO ME ONCE, BUT IT WAS EITHER NONSENSE OR GENIUS OF SUCH AN ORDER THAT I COULDN'T FOLLOW IT...
YOU SAID HE HAD A SON.
VERY BRIGHT BOY.
IT WAS A TRAGEDY...
I SPENT A LOT OF TIME WITH HIM.

I TAUGHT HIM SOME MATHEMATICS AT, OH, GRADUATE DEGREE LEVEL.
HE WAS BRILLIANT.
I THINK HE WOULD RATHER HAVE SPENT THE TIME WITH HIS FATHER.
BUT THINGS WERE NOT HAPPY...
EINSTEIN THOUGHT BLAKE'S EXPERIMENT WAS AN IRRESPONSIBLE COMPROMISE WITH POLITICS...
BUT BLAKE WAS A PROFOUNDLY STUBBORN MAN. AND ON THE DAY OF THE ECLIPSE...

... DISASTER...

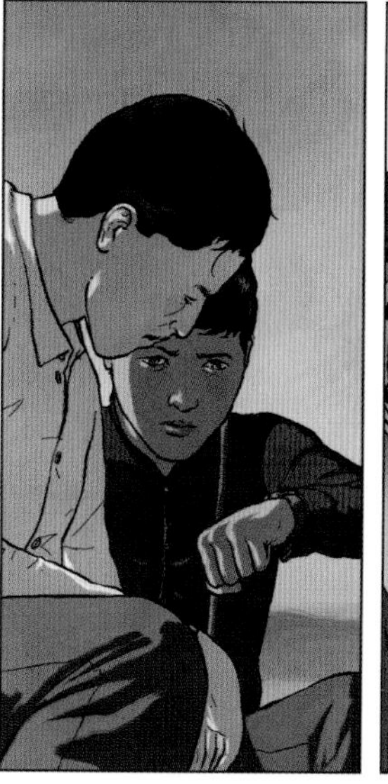

BLAKE'S EXPERIMENT APPARENTLY DEPENDED ON THE PRECISE TIME OF THE MAXIMUM ECLIPSE.

THE RESULT WAS TERRIBLE...

CLICK

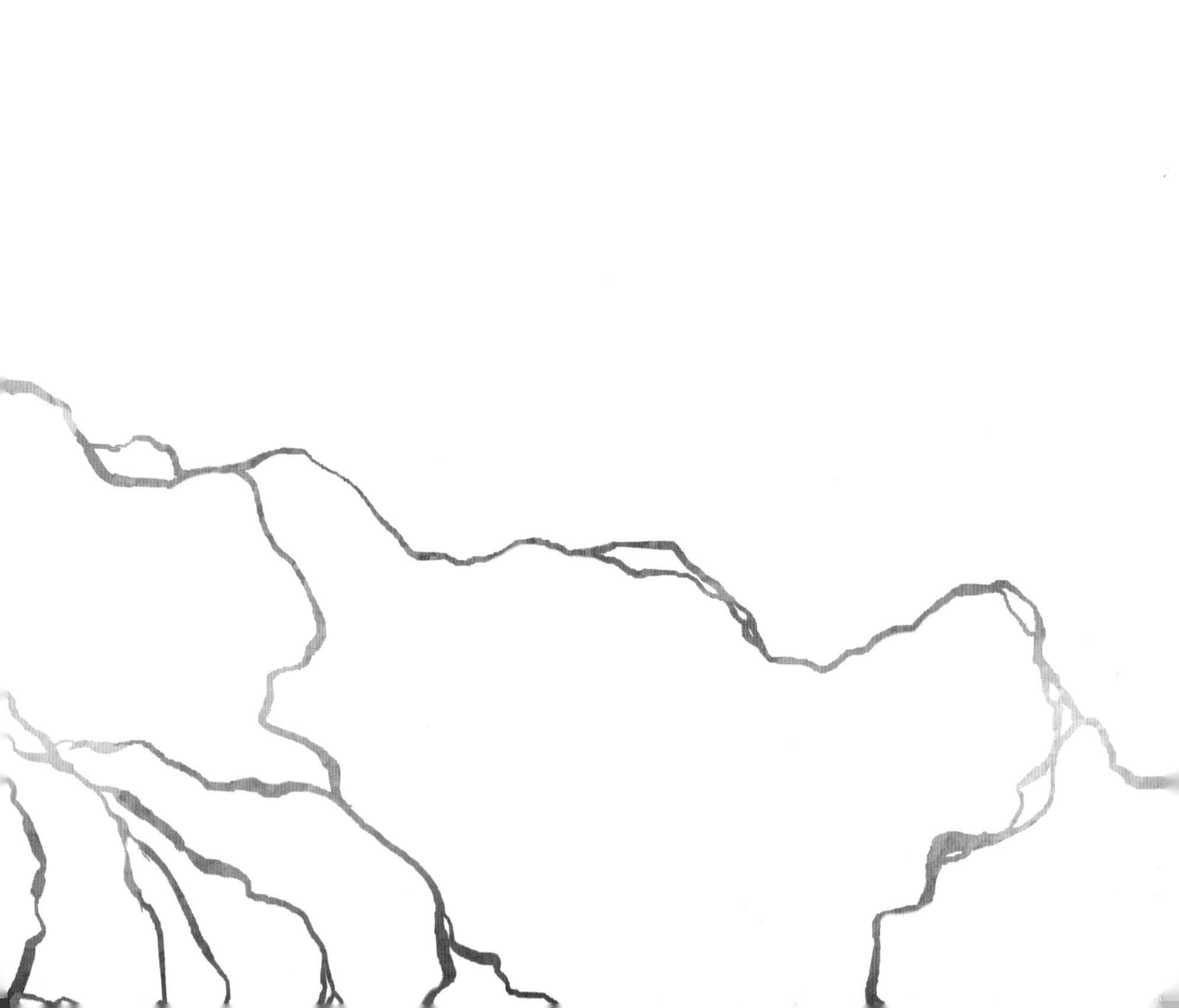

WHAT HAPPENED?
THERE WAS AN EXPLOSION – PERFECTLY SILENT – THE LIGHT SEEMED TO SHINE THROUGH US ALL LIKE X-RAYS...
A MOMENT LATER, WHEN OUR EYES ADJUSTED, WE FOUND OURSELVES IN THE MIDDLE OF THE DENSEST FOG I'D EVER KNOWN.
AND THE BOY WAS... GONE...
THEY SENT A BOAT OUT, IN CASE HE'D FALLEN IN THE WATER, BUT...
NO LUCK.

WE NEVER SAW THE BOY AGAIN.
WHAT HAPPENED TO DR BLAKE? DID HE CONTINUE HIS WORK?
HE WAS SICKENED BY THE WHOLE BUSINESS AFTER THE LOSS OF HIS SON. GAVE UP SCIENCE - TOOK TO BEE-KEEPING, I BELIEVE.
DO YOU REMEMBER ANYTHING ABOUT HIS PROJECT?
WELL...
THERE'S THIS.
WHAT IS IT?

PART OF HIS MACHINE.
WHEN HE LOST HEART AFTER THE BOY DISAPPEARED, I TOOK IT AWAY OUT OF CURIOSITY.
NEVER COULD MAKE ANY SENSE OF IT. CONTRADICTS EVERYTHING I KNOW. TAKE IT IF YOU WANT. I'M TIRED OF TRYING TO WORK IT OUT.
THANK YOU.
I THINK YOU SHOULD GO NOW, SIR. MY FATHER GETS TIRED VERY EASILY.
PROFESSOR, I'M MOST GRATEFUL TO YOU.
YOU LOOKING FOR THAT BOY?
YES, I AM.
WHAT'S YOUR NAME? EH?
BLAKE.
ROGER BLAKE.
TIME'S A STRANGE THING.
GOOD LUCK TO YOU.
THANK YOU.

Danielle Quayle Reid's Apartment, San Francisco

DAMN.
THEY GOT EVERYTHING.

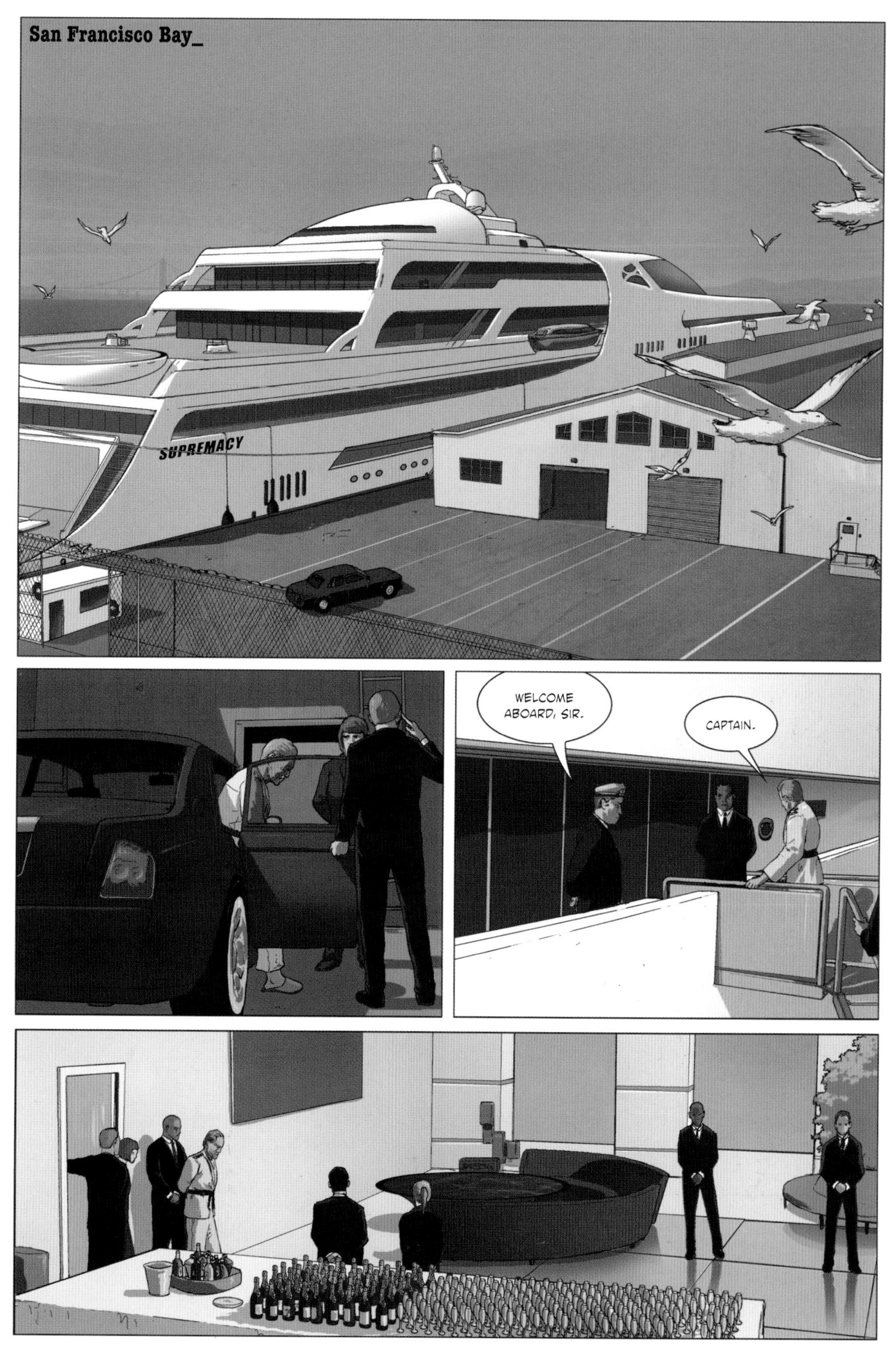
San Francisco Bay_
SUPREMACY
WELCOME ABOARD, SIR.
CAPTAIN.

HENRY, PEOPLE ARE DEVELOPING AN AWKWARD HABIT.
SIR?
THEY WRITE THINGS DOWN IN **NOTEBOOKS** WITH **PENS** AND **PENCILS**. THEY MEET FACE TO FACE AND TALK TO EACH OTHER. THEY PUT LETTERS IN THE **MAIL**.
AFTERNOON, SIR. DID YOU HAVE A GOOD SESSION AT THE DOJO?
THANK YOU, YES, BILL.
THIS IS ***NOT WHAT I WANT.*** I INVENT THE MOST ADVANCED AND INTERCONNECTED COMMUNICATION NETWORK IN HISTORY AND THEY TURN THEIR BACKS ON IT.
NOT WHAT I WANT!
WHAT HAVE YOU GOT FOR ME?
I SUGGEST WE START WITH THE LADY HERSELF ...
DANIELLE QUAYLE REID, THIRTY-ONE YEARS OLD, HARVARD LAW SCHOOL, CURRENTLY WORKING —
THE HELL WITH WHO SHE IS. TELL ME WHAT SHE'S DISCOVERED ABOUT THIS TIME-TRAVELLING SHIP.
BILL?
Algiers 1614
Port of Spain 1699
Rio de Janeiro 1733
Reykjavik 1767
Seattle 1885
Surabaya 1857
Whitby 1906
Darwin 1953
Valparaiso 1966
Colombo 2010
Reykjavik 1767
Stockholm 1856
Whitby 1906
Seattle 1885
Algiers 1614
Alexandria 1801
San Francisco 1973
Port of Spain 1699
Colombo 2010
Surabaya 1857
Darwin 1953
Rio de Janeiro 1733
Valparaiso 1966
THESE ARE THE SIGHTINGS OF THE *MARY ALICE* WE HAVE SO FAR.

TWENTY CONFIRMED IN TOTAL, SIR.
ANY SHE HAS THAT WE DIDN'T?
JUST NANTUCKET, 1833.
PUT IT UP, PUT IT UP.
CLEVER GIRL. SHE GOT A BOYFRIEND, HUSBAND? GIRLFRIEND?
SHE'S A WIDOW. HER HUSBAND DIED THREE YEARS AGO IN A CAR CRASH.
HMM. WHAT ELSE DID YOU FIND?
PICTURES, FIRST-HAND ACCOUNTS, DATES, SOURCES.
AND SHE HAD COPIES OF VARIOUS SHIPPING DOCUMENTS – CARGO MANIFESTS, THAT KIND OF THING.
SHE'S BEEN GATHERING THIS STUFF FOR A WHILE.

WHY? WHY? WHAT DOES SHE WANT? AND THAT FIASCO IN LONDON...
WE DON'T KNOW, SIR. SHE APPEARS TO BE LOOKING FOR A PATTERN. WE COULD BRING HER IN – INVITE HER TO ANSWER SOME QUESTIONS...
PATTERN, HA! IF ONLY IT WERE THAT SIMPLE.
HOW MANY OF THESE THINGS HAVE WE SOLD NOW?
JUST OVER TWO BILLION, SIR.
AND OUR NEAREST COMPETITOR?
NOT EVEN A QUARTER OF THAT.
THAT'S FIVE HUNDRED MILLION PEOPLE NOT BUYING MY PRODUCT, JULIE.
THERE'S A BOY ABOARD THAT SCHOONER WHO KNOWS THINGS THAT COULD RUIN US, AND HAS SOMETHING THAT COULD DESTROY OUR COMPETITION. AND I WANT IT.
A DEVICE CONTAINING SECRET KNOWLEDGE.
BUT, AS YOUTH IS WASTED ON THE YOUNG, SO TIME-TRAVEL IS WASTED ON THE MARY ALICE.
downloading
SINCE SHE DICTATES THE TERMS OF ALL OUR ENCOUNTERS, ALL WE CAN DO IS WAIT.
WE'RE READY FOR HER THIS TIME, SIR.
THE EVENT ORGANISERS ARE HERE, MR DAHLBERG.
VERY APPROPRIATE. THIS PRODUCT LAUNCH MUST GO AHEAD WITHOUT ANY MISTAKES. THE WORLD WILL BE WATCHING.
THIS WILL HERALD A NEW ERA IN HUMAN COMMUNICATION.
WE HAVE EVERYTHING UNDER CONTROL, SIR.
WHILE I DETEST TURNING MY SHIP OVER TO A RABBLE OF FREELOADING WASTRELS, THIS PARTY MUST BE THE GREATEST THING SAN FRANCISCO BAY HAS SEEN SINCE THE CONSTRUCTION OF THE GOLDEN GATE BRIDGE.
WE UNDERSTAND, SIR.
MAKE SURE YOU DO.

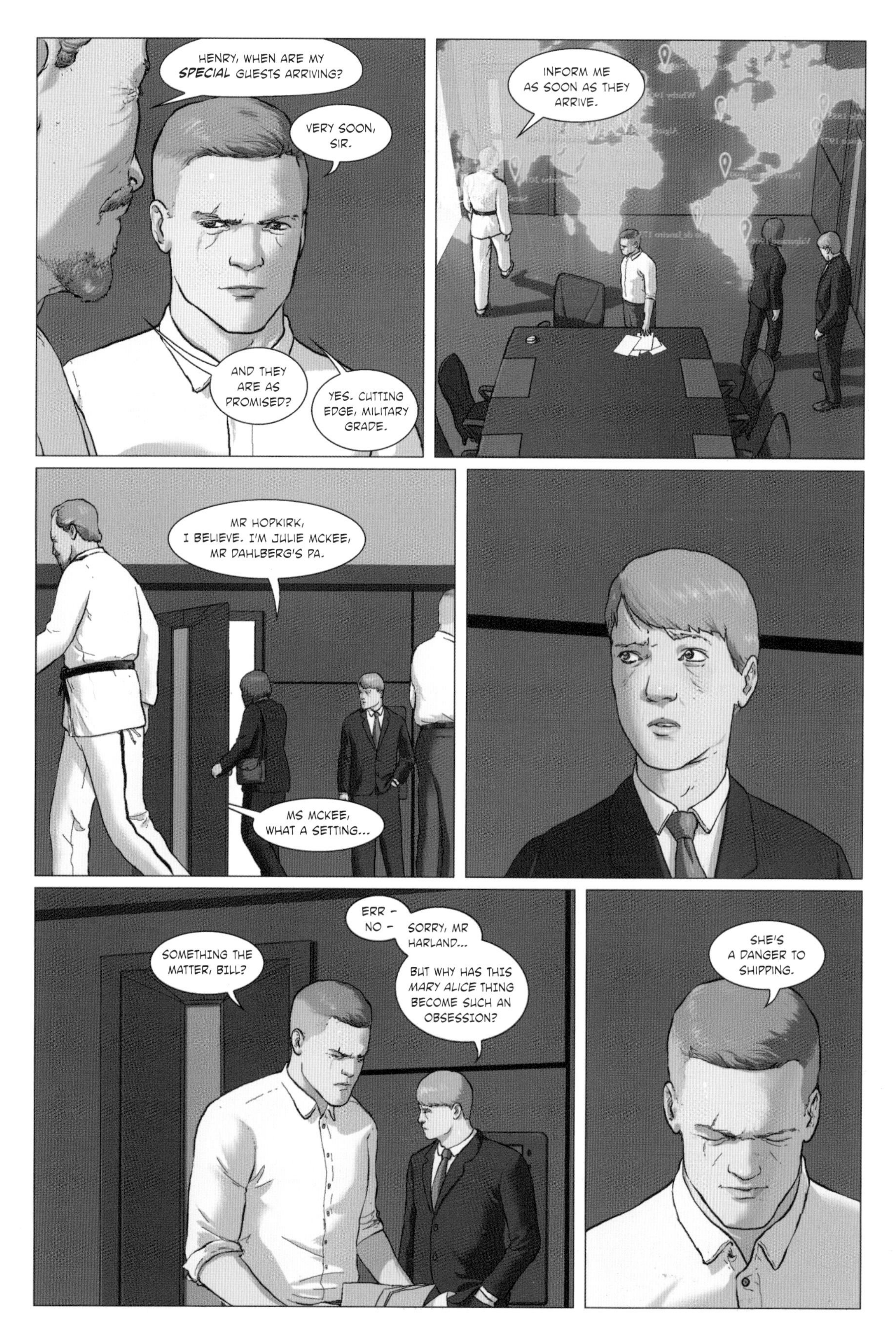
HENRY, WHEN ARE MY SPECIAL GUESTS ARRIVING?
VERY SOON, SIR.
AND THEY ARE AS PROMISED?
YES. CUTTING EDGE, MILITARY GRADE.
INFORM ME AS SOON AS THEY ARRIVE.
MR HOPKIRK, I BELIEVE. I'M JULIE MCKEE, MR DAHLBERG'S PA.
MS MCKEE, WHAT A SETTING...
SOMETHING THE MATTER, BILL?
ERR – NO –
SORRY, MR HARLAND...
BUT WHY HAS THIS MARY ALICE THING BECOME SUCH AN OBSESSION?
SHE'S A DANGER TO SHIPPING.

Danielle Quayle Reid's Apartment, San Francisco_
OK, THAT'S DONE.
NO ONE'S GONNA BREAK THROUGH THAT.
THANK YOU.
CLICK
DDDDDRRRRIIIINNGGGGG

DANIELLE!
HOW'RE THINGS?
OH, CHRIS, HI.
THANKS FOR COMING OVER.
THEY WERE THOROUGH, YOU KNOW? THEY JUST TOOK THE MARY ALICE STUFF – ALL OF IT. EVERY PHOTOCOPY, EVERY CLIPPING...
YOU GOT ANY IDEA WHO DID IT?
NO, NOT REALLY. SCHWARTZ?
WELL, THIS MIGHT CHEER YOU UP.
WHAT IS IT?
I SAW IT BY CHANCE. AN INCIDENT REPORT FROM FIJI. AN AUSTRALIAN FAMILY SAILING ROUND THE WORLD GOT CAUGHT IN A STORM, AND THE DAUGHTER WAS WASHED OVERBOARD.
THEY MADE THEIR WAY TO FIJI...
YEAH, YEAH...
OH!
JEEZ!
I GET IT!
"THE 12-YEAR-OLD SON, ROY, CLAIMS THAT HE SAW AN OLD-TYPE SCHOONER IN THE FOG, AND A BOY WEARING A RED SHIRT..."
THIS IS GREAT. THIS IS GOLD!
WHAT ARE YOU DOING?
I'M BUYING A TICKET TO FIJI.
WHAT?
WHAT ABOUT THE JOB?
SCREW THE JOB.

Mary Alice, Rock of Gibraltar_

IT'S SO HOT...

I CAN'T SLEEP. AND I CAN'T GET A MESSAGE TO MUM AND DAD BECAUSE IT SEEMS I'VE WOUND UP ON A TIME-TRAVELLING SHIP FROM THE 1920S...

ARE THESE PEOPLE CRAZY?
JOHN DOESN'T SEEM CRAZY...
OH, THIS HAMMOCK! TALK ABOUT UNCOMFORTABLE ...

I JUST NEED TO –
OH!

OW! DAMN! THAT HURT...

THUNK
OW!
THIS BLOODY SHIP...

KEEP AT IT JOHN.
I'M TRYING BUT...
DON'T WORRY, LAD.
THERE'S A PIECE MISSING.
KEEP QUIET AND KEEP STILL. WE'RE IN DANGER.
WHAT'S THE PROBLEM?
DEPENDS WHAT YEAR IT IS. LISTEN.
PLAP
PLAP
PLAP
SPLISH

PLAP
PLAP
SPLISH
PLAP
PLAP
SPLISH
PLAP

OARS? SOMEONE ROWING?
MM.

WHAT ARE WE LOOKING FOR?

PIRATES.

IT'S BARBARIES, DAVY.
YOU SURE?

CERTAIN. THEY'RE DOING WHAT THEY DONE IN MY VILLAGE – ROWING SLOW AND QUIET. THEY'RE ON A SLAVING RAID.

SERENA, GO BELOW DECKS AND STAY THERE. DICK, TAKE THE WHEEL. AS SOON AS WE GOT ANY WAY, HARD A-STARBOARD.
AYE, DAVY.
WHAT'S JOHN DOING?

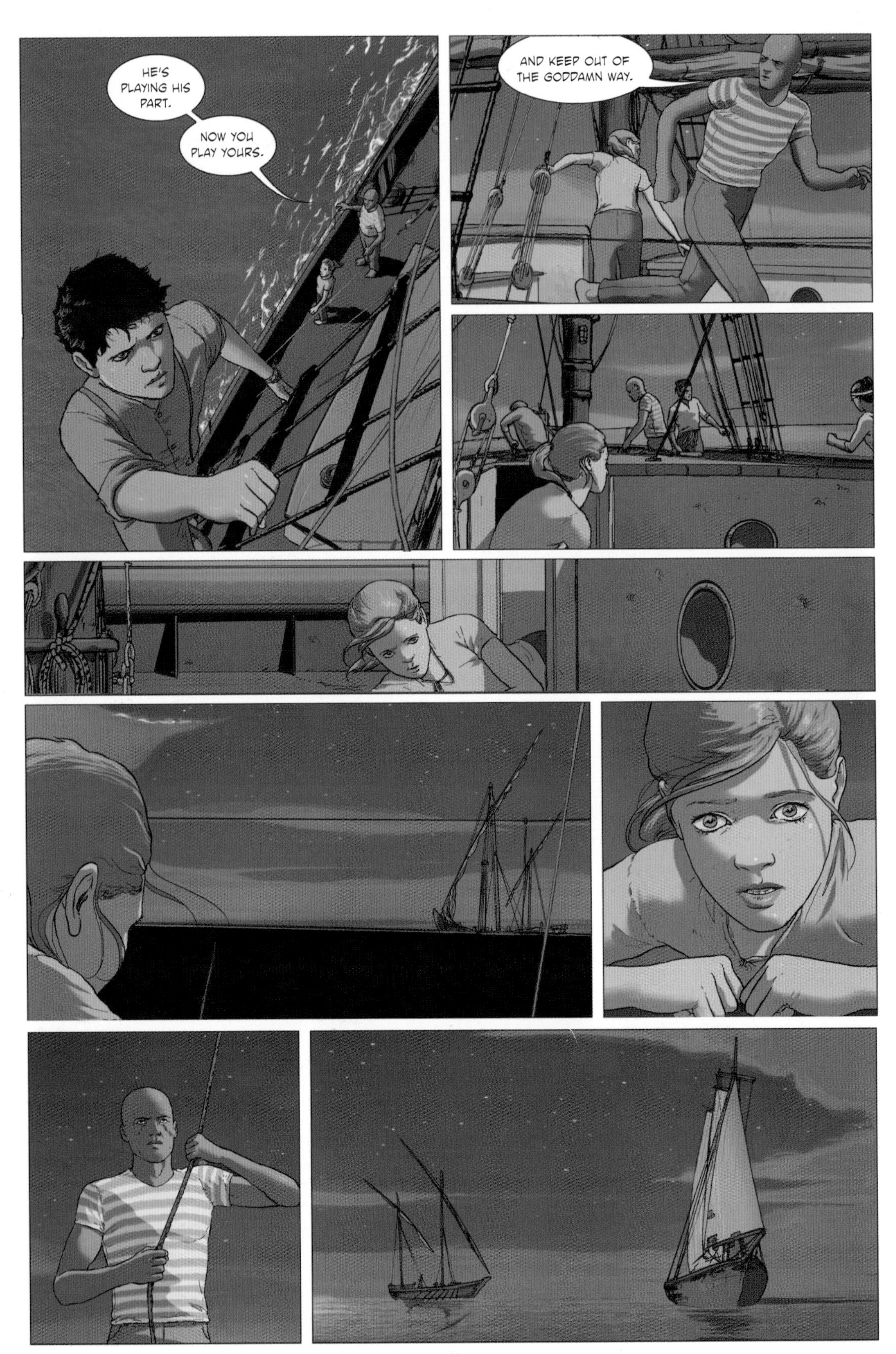
HE'S PLAYING HIS PART.
NOW YOU PLAY YOURS.
AND KEEP OUT OF THE GODDAMN WAY.

WAIT FOR MY SIGNAL, LADS.
GET READY!
PREPARE FOR ATTACK!
NOW.
KLAK
DING DING DING DING DING
CLANG
BINK
NNNNNNYYYYYYYYUUUUURRR
NNNNNNYYYYYYYYUUUUURRRRRRRRRRRNN
NNNNNNYYYYYYYYUUUUURRRRRRRRRRRNN
?
WHAT'S THAT?
OH, GOD!

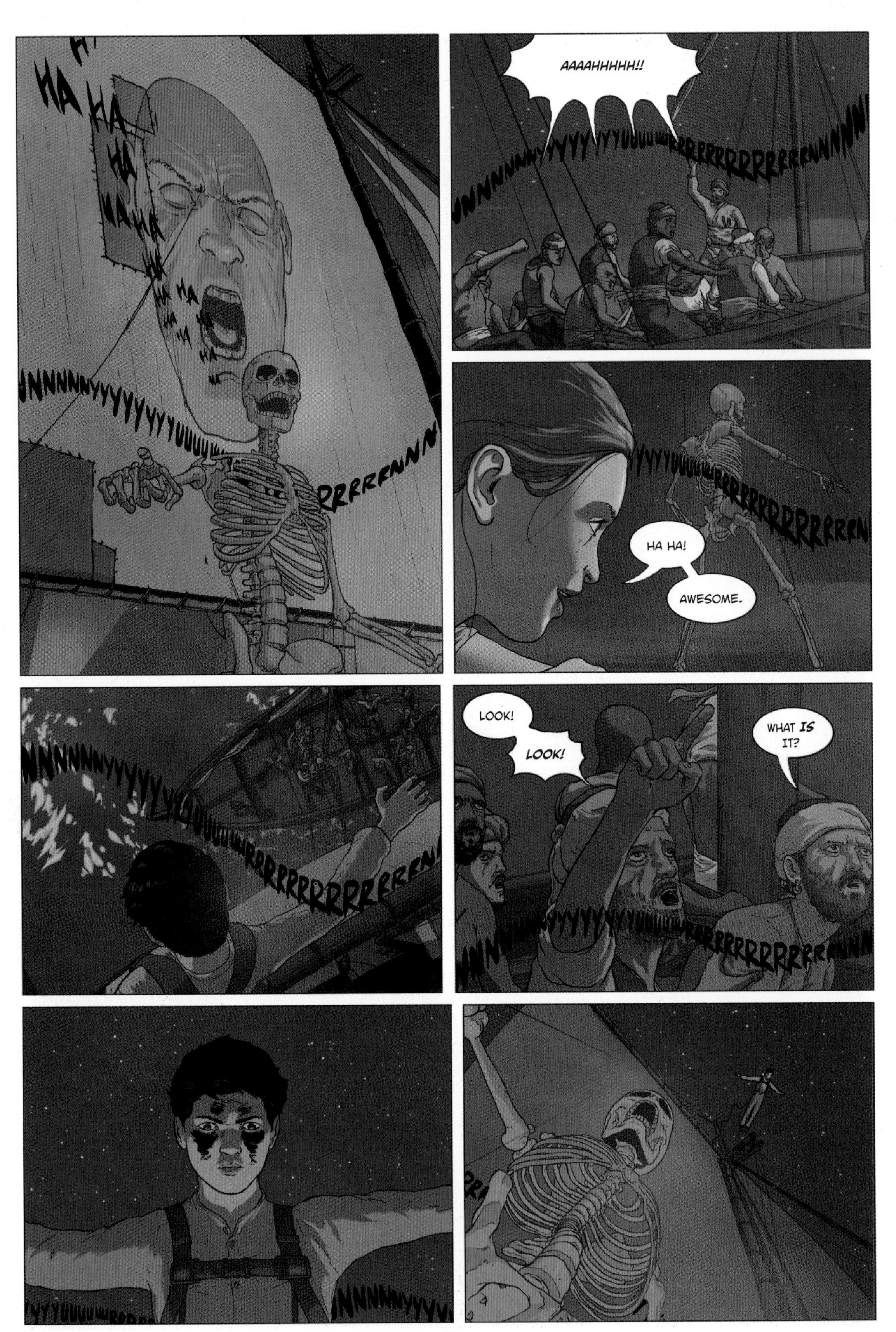
HA
HA
HA
HA
HA
HA HA
HA
HA
HA
HA
HA
NNNNNNYYYYYYYYUUUUWRRRRFNNNN
AAAAHHHHH!!
NNNNNNNYYYYYYYUUUUWRRRRRRRRRRRRRRRNNNNN
YYYYUUUUWRRRRRRRRRRRRRRRRN
HA HA!
AWESOME.
NNNNNNYYYYYYUUUUWRRRRRRRRRRRRFN
LOOK!
LOOK!
WHAT IS IT?
NNNNNNYYYYYYYYYUUUUWRRRRRRRRRRRRRRNNN
NNNNNYYYV
YYYUUUUWRRR

IT'S A SEA-DJINN!
NNNNNyyyy
RETREAT!
AAAAAH!
RETREAT!
ABANDON SHIP!
CLUNK
CLANK
SPUT
PUT
PUT PUT
O, INFERNUM!
OH, HELL!
THE GENERATOR ...

VENI IN, SATUS!
COME ON, START!
OH NO...
THIS HAD BETTER WORK.
AAAAAAAAAAAAAAAAAAAA
ABANDON SHIP!
AAAAAAAAAAAAAAAAAAAAAAAAAAAAAAAAAAAAARRRGGHHHHH

Admiralty, London_
I'VE BEEN LOOKING INTO THIS SHELL CORPORATION, THE PENTAGRAM FOUNDATION.
THE DOCUMENTS YOU RETRIEVED ALL CONCERN THE GHOST SHIP, THE *MARY ALICE*. AND, ROGER... THEY DATE BACK CENTURIES.
I KNOW.
YOU DO?
I COULDN'T BEGIN TO EXPLAIN IT TO YOU. NOT YET.
WELL, THIS HARLAND CHARACTER IS DEFINITELY ON THE LEASH FOR SOMEONE.
I THOUGHT THEY WERE KEEPING THEIR TRACKS WELL COVERED.
BUT THEN I FOUND THIS.
SO HENRY HARLAND IS WORKING FOR DAHLBERG?
BUT ISN'T DAHLBERG...
WORLD AWAITS DAHLBERG LAUNCH
By Alice Thomas
YES, JUST ABOUT THE RICHEST MAN IN THE WORLD.
SO THE FAMOUS CARLOS DAHLBERG IS LOOKING FOR THE ***MARY ALICE***? BUT WHY?
HE'S A BUSINESSMAN AND SHE APPEARS TO BE A TIME-TRAVELLING SHIP - THINK OF THE THE POSSIBILITIES...
AND HE'S NOT THE ONLY ONE.
A DANIELLE QUAYLE REID AT THE INTERNATIONAL MARINE ORGANIZATION IN SAN FRANCISCO HAS BEEN TAKING QUITE AN INTEREST TOO. WE'RE PUTTING TOGETHER A FILE ON HER NOW.
THIS *IS* GETTING INTERESTING.
OH, AND I ALMOST FORGOT.
WHAT IN GOD'S NAME IS THAT?
I WAS HOPING YOU COULD TELL ME.

WHERE DID YOU GET IT?
SOMEONE GAVE IT TO ME.
IT REMINDS ME OF THOSE DIAGRAMS WE USED TO TRY AND DRAW TO EXPLAIN FIVE- OR SIX-DIMENSIONAL SPACE...
YEAH. EXACTLY.
WELL, I JUST DON'T BELIEVE IT. THE WEIRDEST DAMN THING...
TAKE IT AWAY. IT'S DISTURBING MY WORLD-VIEW.
I KNOW WHAT YOU MEAN. THANKS, TOM.
BE CAREFUL, ROGER, IF YOU'RE DEALING WITH DAHLBERG. WORD IS HE'S BARKING MAD.
OH AND ROGER, YOUR APPARATOR...
YES?
I'VE THROWN MINE AWAY.
WHY?
I THINK HE CAN READ THEM...
DAHLBERG CAN READ THE APPARATORS?
IT'S THE NETWORK. EACH ONE JUST ACTS AS A NODE TO SPREAD IT EVEN FURTHER. HIS OWN GLOBAL WIRELESS NETWORK!
BUT HE'S SOLD BILLIONS ...
YUP.
LIKE I SAID, I THREW MINE AWAY.

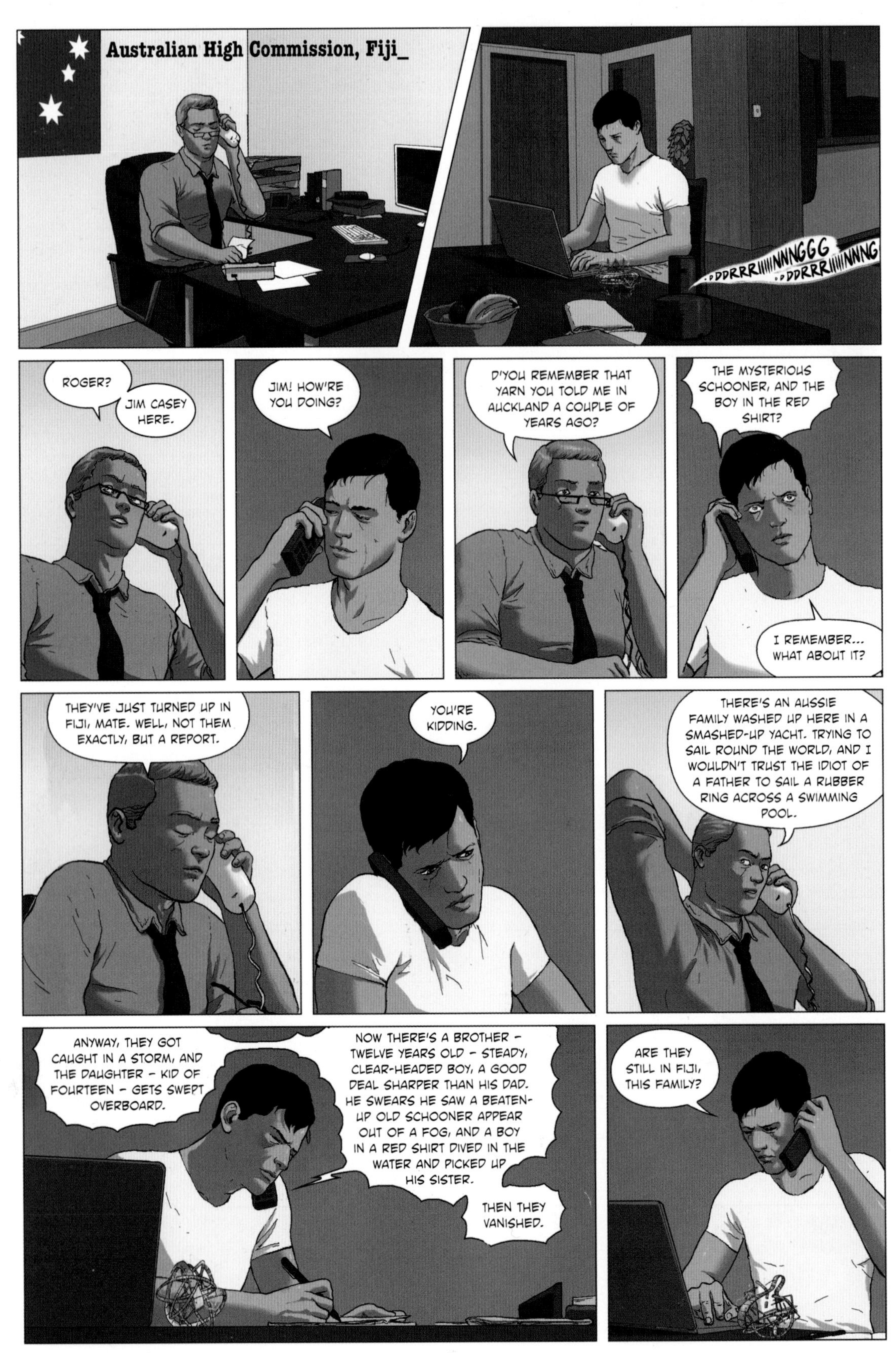
Australian High Commission, Fiji_
DDRRRIIIIINNNGGG
DDRRRIIIIINNNG
ROGER?
JIM CASEY HERE.
JIM! HOW'RE YOU DOING?
D'YOU REMEMBER THAT YARN YOU TOLD ME IN AUCKLAND A COUPLE OF YEARS AGO?
THE MYSTERIOUS SCHOONER, AND THE BOY IN THE RED SHIRT?
I REMEMBER... WHAT ABOUT IT?
THEY'VE JUST TURNED UP IN FIJI, MATE. WELL, NOT THEM EXACTLY, BUT A REPORT.
YOU'RE KIDDING.
THERE'S AN AUSSIE FAMILY WASHED UP HERE IN A SMASHED-UP YACHT. TRYING TO SAIL ROUND THE WORLD, AND I WOULDN'T TRUST THE IDIOT OF A FATHER TO SAIL A RUBBER RING ACROSS A SWIMMING POOL.
ANYWAY, THEY GOT CAUGHT IN A STORM, AND THE DAUGHTER – KID OF FOURTEEN – GETS SWEPT OVERBOARD.
NOW THERE'S A BROTHER – TWELVE YEARS OLD – STEADY, CLEAR-HEADED BOY, A GOOD DEAL SHARPER THAN HIS DAD. HE SWEARS HE SAW A BEATEN-UP OLD SCHOONER APPEAR OUT OF A FOG, AND A BOY IN A RED SHIRT DIVED IN THE WATER AND PICKED UP HIS SISTER.
THEN THEY VANISHED.
ARE THEY STILL IN FIJI, THIS FAMILY?

THEY'RE NOT GOING ANYWHERE IN THAT YACHT, MATE. THEY'RE HERE FOR A WHILE YET.
I'VE GOT TO TAKE CARE OF SOMETHING IN SAN FRANCISCO, BUT I'LL SEE YOU ON...
CLIK TAP TAP
... WEDNESDAY.
AND I'LL BUY YOU A DRINK.
OH, YOU'RE COMING OVER? GREAT!
DON'T LET 'EM GO TILL I'VE MET THEM.
CRACK
SIZZLE
POK
CRACKLE
SAMMY? LAST NIGHT – THOSE PIRATES – HAVE YOU SEEN THEM BEFORE?
MAYBE NOT SAME ONES. BUT BARBARY PIRATES, YOU BET. VERY BAD MEN. ALL THROUGH SEVENTEEN, EIGHTEEN CENTURY. BIG DANGER.
WHERE IS BARBARY? WHAT DO THEY DO?
NORTH AFRICA. THEY TAKE SLAVES. LIKE DICK – THEY TOOK HIM FROM VILLAGE IN ENGLAND.
THEY WENT TO ENGLAND?
ICELAND EVEN. THEY TAKE SLAVES, MAKE THEM ROW, SELL THEM. AND GIRLS...
WHAT?
FOR HAREM. YOU KNOW? WHEN DAVY SAY 'GET BELOW', LAST NIGHT, YOU SHOULD GO.
THAT'S WHY.

IT WAS A GOOD SCREAM THOUGH, WASN'T IT?
THEY ARE VERY BAD MEN. DON'T TAKE CHANCE.
BUT WE'RE IN A DIFFERENT TIME NOW, RIGHT?
MAYBE. CAN'T TELL FROM SEA.
ONE WAVE JUS' LOOK LIKE ANOTHER.
I GUESS SO...
AND THERE'S ANOTHER THING: WHY ARE YOU GUYS ALWAYS DOING CARPENTRY? EVERY DAY THERE'S MORE HAMMERING AND SAWING GOING ON.
SHE AN OLD SHIP, WE GOTTA KEEP HER FIXED...
HMM.
HOW ART THOU, SERENA?
RIGHT MERRY, THANK'EE, DICK.
YOU GOT HER SPEAKING SEVENTEENTH CENTURY.
SHE CAN'T SPEAK ROMAN, THOUGH.
ROMAN LINGUA IS EASY. ANGLISH IS B*******.
WHAT YOU MAKING THERE, MARCUS?
ISS A MOUSETRAP. WHAT IT LOOK LIKE?
AH.
THOUSAND-YEAR-OLD MICE ABOARD TOO, EH?

YOUR COFFEE, CAPTAIN...
TEN POINTS STARBOARD, CAP'N!
TEN POINTS STARBOARD, CHARLIE.
AYE, AYE, SIR. WHERE D'YOU THINK WE ARE, CAP'N?
I THINK THIS IS THE PACIFIC. IT FEELS PACIFIC.
CAPTAIN, IF YOU HAD A – ONE OF THOSE THINGS – YOU HOLD IT UP AND LOOK THROUGH IT –
A SEXTANT.
YEAH. ONE OF THOSE, YOU COULD TELL WHERE WE WERE.
I'VE GOT A BEAUTIFUL SEXTANT. I TAKE IT OUT AND POLISH IT ONCE A WEEK.
BUT IT'S NO GOD-DAMNED USE WITHOUT ANY IDEA WHAT THE GODDAMNED TIME IS.
WHAT'S IT LOOK LIKE, DAVY?
LOOKS LIKE BIRDHEAD ISLAND, CAP'N.
IS THAT RIGHT? INTERESTING...
INTERESTING HOW?
WE WERE JUST IN THIS NECK OF THE WOODS.
WHY IS *THAT* INTERESTING?
BECAUSE WE'RE A TIME-TRAVELLING SHIP. AND THERE'S A LOT OF TIME TO TRAVEL IN. BUT SOMETIMES THE *MARY ALICE* TAKES US TO THE SAME TIME AND PLACE AGAIN AND AGAIN. AND SHE SEEMS TO LIKE FIJI
SO...
ARE YOU THE CAPTAIN OR IS SHE?
ENOUGH CHATTER. DAVY, YOU AND CHARLIE GO AND HOIST THE FORESAIL.
SERENA, TAKE THE WHEEL.

ME?
NO, THE OTHER SERENA, THE SMART ONE.
...
CAPTAIN... WHO'S JOHN? IS HE FROM YOUR TIME? OR...
JOHN BLAKE IS THE REASON WE'RE IN THIS CONDITION. HE'S ALSO THE ONLY WAY WE'LL EVER GET OUT OF IT.
SERENA, WHAT WERE YOU DOING SAILING ACROSS THE PACIFIC OCEAN?
IT WAS MY DAD'S IDEA... HE BOUGHT THIS BIG BOAT AND HE THOUGHT WE COULD SAIL ROUND THE WORLD. HIM AND MUM AND MY BROTHER, ROY...
IS YOUR FATHER A SAILOR?
NO. NOT REALLY. THAT'S THE PROBLEM. WE'VE SAILED AROUND SYDNEY HARBOUR, BUT...
HE DIDN'T...
WE NEVER...
HEY, HEY. STOW THAT. NO TEARS ON THE *MARY ALICE*. COMPANY ORDERS.
YOU KNOW, SERENA, WE MIGHT FIND WE'RE IN YOUR PRESENT DAY WHEN WE GET TO FIJI.
BUT... HOW COME? I THOUGHT YOU DIDN'T KNOW WHERE YOU'D END UP.
WE DON'T.
BUT *MARY ALICE*... LIKE I SAID, SHE HAS A MIND OF HER OWN.

SEE THAT SPECK OF LAND UP AHEAD?
IS THAT FIJI?
NO, BUT IT'S CLOSE. STEER A LITTLE EAST OF THAT.
EAST? WHICH WAY'S THAT?
CAPTAIN?
Dahlberg Warehouse, San Francisco_

SIR, DANIELLE QUAYLE REID'S APPARATOR JUST WOKE UP.
BOOP... BOOP... BOOP...
WHAT'S SHE DOING?

BUYING AN AIRLINE TICKET TO FIJI.
CALL HENRY.

SIR?
HENRY, GO TO THE INTERNATIONAL MARINE ORGANIZATION AND ASK THAT FOOL SCHWARTZ ABOUT FIJI.
SOMETHING'S HAPPENED THERE. FIND OUT WHAT IT IS.
OH, AND, HENRY – LITTLE DANIELLE HAS BOUGHT A TICKET FOR FIJI. I DON'T WANT HER TO GO.
I UNDERSTAND, MR DAHLBERG.
AH.
LOOKS LIKE MY FIRST SPECIAL GUEST.
ARE THOSE WHAT I THINK THEY ARE?
WELL, IF THEY ARE, WE'LL NEVER KNOW. THEY WON'T UNLOAD THAT TRUCK TILL THE BUILDING'S EMPTY.
BILL, I'M GETTING WORRIED. IF HE'S *THAT* CRAZY, WHAT DO WE DO?
I'VE SPENT A LOT OF TIME THINKING ABOUT THAT. AND I STILL DON'T KNOW.

San Francisco
International Airport_
3
2
1

BAF

INTERESTING PICTURE.
OH - THANKS -
I THINK SO.
- THANKS.

Becky's
MS QUAYLE REID?
YES?
WHAT IS IT?
WOULD YOU MIND COMING WITH US? THERE'S A SMALL PROBLEM WITH YOUR PASSPORT.
"...HENRY HARLAND, KNOWN PENTAGRAM ASSOCIATE AND EXPERT ON ENHANCED INTERROGATION TECHNIQUES..."
Henry Harland
THERE'S NOTHING WRONG WITH MY PASSPORT –
JUST A QUICK ADMINISTRATIVE CHECK. I NEED YOU TO COME THIS WAY.
WHO ARE YOU, ANYWAY?
IF YOU WANT TO CATCH YOUR PLANE, YOU NEED TO COME WITH US.
WHAT ARE YOU DOING?
PLEASE DON'T MAKE A FUSS. IT WILL TAKE SO MUCH LONGER...

HEY!
TAKE YOUR HANDS OFF ME!
WHERE ARE YOU TAKING –
HEY!
WHAT DO YOU WANT? WHO ARE YOU?
LET ME OUT OF HERE! HOW DARE YOU –
AAGGHH!
MGF – MMG
MFF
WHO –

AAH
THWAP
WAK
UFF
AARGHH!

IN MY BACKPACK THERE'S A ROLL OF DUCT TAPE. BIND THEIR HANDS TOGETHER AS TIGHT AS YOU CAN.
I... OK.
I WARN YOU, WHOEVER YOU ARE –
IF YOU KNEW. IF YOU KNEW WHO YOU WERE DEALING –
≠MGGGFFN MMG≠
LET'S GO.
WHO ARE YOU?
ROGER BLAKE, ROYAL NAVY.
DANIELLE QUAYLE REID. UNEMPLOYED.
QUAYLE... THE SKIPPER OF THE *MARY ALICE*.
MY GREAT-GRANDFATHER. HOW D'YOU KNOW?
YOU'RE GOING TO FIJI, RIGHT?
THAT'S RIGHT. HOW –
LET'S NOT MISS THAT PLANE.

The *Supremacy*, San Francisco_

...
PICK UP, HENRY, YOU IDIOT!

BOOP
BOOP
BOOP
BOOP
BOOP
WHAT CAN I DO FOR YOU, MR DAHLBERG?

WHERE'S HENRY? WHY ISN'T HE ANSWERING?
I DON'T KNOW, SIR. WOULD YOU LIKE ME TO –
FIND OUT WHERE HE IS.

DEATHWATCH MISSILE
11 - 13 - 4 - 3
X 4
PZLJRF 11089 - - COUNTER

Suva, Fiji_
FLINK
THANKS, BOSS!
WELL? YOU INTERESTED?
COURSE I AM!
TWENTY-FIRST – THAT'S...
THAT'S RIGHT! IT'S TODAY!
THIS IS... I DON'T BELIEVE IT! THEY'RE HERE! THEY'RE SAFE!
I TOLD YOU MARY ALICE HAD A MIND OF HER OWN.
AUSTRALIAN WRECK
FAMILY IN MYSTERY SHIP CLAIM
MR AND MRS HENDERSON...
TRAGIC LOSS OF THEIR DAUGHTER, SERENA ...
... STAYING AT THE AUSTRALIAN HIGH COMMISSION.
WELL, THAT'S WHERE YOU'D BETTER GO, SERENA.

JOHN'LL TAKE YOU.
OH... YEAH. RIGHT. WELL...
THANKS, CAPTAIN. I... ENJOYED SAILING WITH YOU.
IT WAS A PLEASURE, SERENA. I HOPE WE'RE AROUND NEXT TIME YOU FALL IN THE OCEAN.
SO DO I.
UMM... WELL, I HAVEN'T GOT ANY LUGGAGE, SO...
IT'S THE RIGHT DATE FOR YOU?
YEAH. EVERYTHING'S... RIGHT.
CAPTAIN, I HOPE YOU FIND YOUR WAY HOME, I REALLY DO.
THANK YOU, SERENA.
AND LISTEN: YOU WERE RESCUED BY A FISHING BOAT - PLAY DOWN THIS MYSTERY SHIP NONSENSE. THIS IS A DANGEROUS TIME FOR US.
I'LL REMEMBER.
THE RIGHT DAY, JOHN. WHAT D'YOU THINK OF THAT?
THERE'S STILL SOMETHING MISSING, CAP'N. SOMETHING I HAVEN'T WORKED OUT.
YOU BE SURE TO LET US KNOW WHEN YOU DO. IN THE MEANTIME, GO WITH SERENA - HELP HER FIND THE WAY.
DON'T TAKE TOO LONG.

SO, WHAT HAPPENS WHEN YOU GUYS COME ASHORE? I MEAN, YOU HAVEN'T GOT PASSPORTS AND STUFF.
THEY USUALLY SEND ME.
WHY?
I CAN RUN FAST.
OK?
NOT BAD, FOR A GUY WHO'S 160 YEARS OLD OR WHATEVER YOU ARE –
The Supremacy_
AND WHERE'S YOUR APPARATOR?
HE TOOK IT.
OH, HE TOOK THAT TOO, ALONG WITH YOUR PRIDE AND YOUR DIGNITY AND YOUR PROFESSIONAL COMPETENCE?
WHERE IS IT, BILL?
IT'S BEEN READ AND DESTROYED, MR DAHLBERG.

HEAR THAT, HENRY? READ AND DESTROYED. YOU EVER THINK THE DAY WOULD COME WHEN SOMEONE WOULD TREAT YOU LIKE THAT?
WHO WAS HE?
I DON'T KNOW, MR DAHLBERG. NEVER SEEN HIM BEFORE.
AND WHAT WILL YOU DO IF YOU SEE HIM AGAIN?
KILL HIM.
WELL, YOU'D BETTER BE QUICKER THAN YOU WERE LAST TIME. HOW LONG WERE YOU LYING ON THAT FLOOR, HENRY?
TWELVE HOURS, SIR.
TWELVE HOURS? THE LITTLE LADY MIGHT BE IN FIJI BY THIS TIME. AND YOU WERE SUPPOSED TO STOP HER FROM GOING AT ALL.
WHAT ARE YOU GOING TO DO ABOUT IT?
MILES? GET ME THE US EMBASSY IN FIJI. GET ME THE GUY IN CHARGE OF SECURITY. TELL HIM IF HE WANTS TO KEEP HIS JOB, HE BETTER COME TO THE PHONE RIGHT NOW.
US Embassy, Fiji_
WHY, CERTAINLY, MR HARLAND... YOU GOT IT... RIGHT AWAY, SIR.
AUSTRALIAN... YUP. YOU BET.
J. W. DUPONT
WHAT'S THIS ABOUT, SIR? WHY THE AUSTRALIAN –
JUST GET IN THE DAMN CAR!
VVVVRRRRMMMMMMMMM

ERNATIONAL ARRIVALS
WELCOME TO SUVA!
TAXI?
PLEASE, PLEASE, LET ME.
WHERE YOU WANNA GO, SIR?
THE AUSTRALIAN HIGH COMMISSION. YOU KNOW WHERE THAT IS?
SURE I KNOW. 'BOUT FORTY MINUTES.
BUT HOW DID YOU GET STUCK ON THE *MARY ALICE* IN THE FIRST PLACE?
WELL... MY FATHER WAS A SCIENTIST. HE WAS DOING AN EXPERIMENT CALLED CYCLONE ON A SHIP IN THE ATLANTIC. ANYWAY, SOMETHING WENT WRONG. I WAS ON THE DECK –
WATCH OUT!
RRRRRRRRRRRR
THAT WAS QUICK. THANKS.
IDIOTS!
SO YOUR FATHER WAS DOING THIS EXPERIMENT, AND –
– AND THERE WAS A SUDDEN FLARE OF ENERGY, AND NEXT THING, I WAS IN THE WATER SURROUNDED BY FOG.
AND THE *MARY ALICE*?
AH, THERE WE ARE.

HEY, WHERE ARE YOU GOING?
ONE HOUR PHOTO
ONE SEC.
ONE HOUR PHOTO
OH MY GOD, THEY STILL HAVE THESE?
WHAT ARE YOU GETTING DEVELOPED ANYWAY?
AN INSURANCE POLICY.
HUH?
OK, GREAT. I'LL JUST WAIT HERE THEN.
TAP TAP TAP
BOO!
HEY!
WELL, COME ON - YOU WANT TO FIND YOUR PARENTS OR NOT?
THE HIGH COMMISSION IS UP HERE SOMEWHERE.
THEN YOU BETTER HURRY UP AND FINISH THE STORY.
WELL, AFTER THE... INCIDENT... THE *MARY ALICE* WAS NEARBY... DAVY HAULED ME OUT WHEN I FELL IN THE SEA. THAT'S ABOUT IT.

IS IT HELL ***ABOUT IT***! WHAT ABOUT THIS FOG, AND THE TIME TRAVEL? HUH? YOU THINK YOU CAN KEEP ME IN THE DARK ABOUT THAT? AND WHY ARE YOU GETTING PHOTOS DEVELOPED?
CAPTAIN QUAYLE SAID THIS WAS A DANGEROUS TIME FOR YOU. WHAT'S THAT MEAN?
THAT'S ANOTHER MATTER.
LOOK, I THINK THAT'S THE PLACE WE WANT.
YOU DON'T GET AWAY WITH IT LIKE THAT. ANOTHER MATTER? ***TELL ME***, JOHN! I'VE BEEN A MEMBER OF THE CREW, DAMMIT! I'VE STEERED THE SHIP!
I NEARLY GOT CAPTURED BY THE BARBARY PIRATES!
ONLY BECAUSE YOU WOULDN'T STAY IN YOUR HAMMOCK.
I'M NOT GOING IN TILL YOU TELL ME WHY THIS IS A DANGEROUS TIME FOR THE *MARY ALICE*. WHAT'S GOING ON? WHAT IS THE TRUTH? HUH?
AUSTRALIAN HIGH COMMISSION
TAXI
!
THE BOY IN THE RED SHIRT...

RRRRRRRRRRRRRRRRR
HEY!
RRRRRR
QUICK – THIS IS URGENT: ARE YOU THE BOY FROM THE *MARY ALICE*? AND THE GIRL WHO FELL OVERBOARD?
I'M SERENA HENDERSON, YEAH, AND THIS IS JOHN BLAKE – BUT WHO – ?
LISTEN: MY NAME'S DANIELLE – FROM THE INTERNATIONAL MARINE ORGANIZATION – I'VE BEEN FOLLOWING THE TRACES OF THE *MARY ALICE* FOR A LONG TIME, AND YOU'RE IN DANGER –
KEEP DOWN!
THE *MARY ALICE* HAS BEEN CHASED ALL OVER THE OCEAN. WHY SHOULD WE TRUST YOU?
BECAUSE I KNOW ABOUT EINSTEIN. AND ABOUT **CYCLONE** – AND CAPTAIN QUAYLE –
LOOK!
OUT OF THE WAY, SIR!
WHERE THE HELL D'YOU THINK YOU'RE GOING?
MUM! DAD!
THAT'S HIM! THAT'S THE KID –
HEY, YOU! STOP THERE!

SERENA!
OH, DARLING –
WHAT ARE YOU DOING, YOU MONGREL? THAT'S MY DAUGHTER!
STAND BACK! US INTELLIGENCE. THIS IS A SECURITY –
WHAK
YOU ENTER AUSTRALIAN TERRITORY AND THREATEN AN AUSTRALIAN CITIZEN, AND I'LL TEACH YOU SOME AUSTRALIAN INTELLIGENCE, YOU HOOLIGAN!
SERENA, YOU'RE ALIVE!
BYE, SERENA!
JOHN...
IT'S OK, MUM! I'M ALL RIGHT!
BUT I'VE GOT TO –
SERENA! WAIT –
NOW GET OUT, AND TAKE YOUR BLOODY COWBOYS WITH YOU!

G'DAY, ROGER!
GOOD TO SEE YOU, JIM. WHERE'S YOUR CAR?
WHERE D'YOU WANT TO GO?
TO THE HARBOUR.
WHAT'S ALL THIS ABOUT?
WE'LL EXPLAIN ON THE WAY!

HARMACY+
GK's E-Z BUY

JOHN!
THIS WAY! THEY'RE COMING!

WHAT ARE YOU DOING? GET BACK THERE! GO TO YOUR PARENTS!
NO! I WANT TO HEAR THE REST OF YOUR STORY! NOW COME ON!

THERE THEY ARE!

QUICK!

SORRY!

YOU LITTLE...

HOTEL

WE GOT 'EM!

THEY'RE HEADING INTO THE HOTEL!

ACT NORMAL.

WHAT NOW?
WATCH AND LEARN.
WHAT ARE YOU –
HMM, NEEDS LEMON.
CHOOSE A BOWL. THE MAYONNAISE LOOKS GOOD.
LOOKING FOR US?
BLB
GHA

BAF
SPLAT!
BACK TO THE KITCHEN.
THAT SHOULD DO IT.
SERIOUSLY?!
COME ON!

-AK- DOOR'S JAMMED.

HEY! YOU CAN'T COME BACK HERE!

OW.
-UFF-

WHAT *NOW*?

THIS WAY!

SSSH.
FWEEET
TOK
COME ON - THROUGH THE CAR -

WVVVRRRRMMMMMMMMM

WHUMP

YOU CAN *DRIVE*?
YOU TARZAN, ME CHAUFFEUR.

HOLD TIGHT!

I DIDN'T KNOW GIRLS COULD DRIVE.

WELL, WATCH AND LEARN, MATE.

HOW DO I OPEN THE WINDOW?
PRESS THAT BUTTON!

POKE

POLICE!
WOOWOOWOOWOWOWOWOO
POLICE
WOOWO
SEE THAT RED LIGHT? GO STRAIGHT THROUGH.
BUT IT'S –
JUST DO IT.
TIME TO LIGHTEN THE LOAD.
POLICE
WHAT'RE YOU DOING? WHERE'RE YOU GOING?
TURN RIGHT!
POLICE

TURN LEFT!
THUNK
GO STRAIGHT ON!
HONK
HONK
HONK

CLNG
SHGNG

BONK
I DIDN'T QUITE MEAN THAT...
WHERE NOW? THIS IS FUN.
NEARLY THERE. JUST GOT TO MAKE A SLIGHT DETOUR. HARD LEFT!
HEY!
OK, STOP!
EEEEE
WHAT ARE YOU DOING?
SEE THAT ALLEY? PULL ROUND THERE. I'LL BE THIRTY SECONDS!
ONE HOUR PHOTO
RRRRR
HEY, WHAT ARE YOU –

YOU GOTTA PAY FOR THAT! STOP HIM!
CRASH
WELL, COME ON, WE HAVEN'T GOT ALL DAY.
WWRRRRMMMM
IS THAT THE TIME?
WHAT ARE YOU DOING?
SETTING YOUR WATCH? WHAT ABOUT –
OH!
OH!
OH!
EEEEEEEEEEEE
TURN DOWN THERE, WHERE HE CAME FROM...
YOU SURE?
GO ON!

THERE SHE IS –
THE FOG! WAIT, WHY WERE YOU SETTING YOUR...
OH NO!

MORE OF THEM!

QUICKER NOW.

EEEEEE
YOUR PARENTS ARE HERE – YOU'RE SAFE NOW.
TELL THEM I WAS TRYING TO KIDNAP YOU.
BYE, SERENA.
BUT –
JOHN, *WAIT!*
WHERE'S THIS FOG COME FROM?!
IT'S GONE!
VANISHED –
– SCHOONER –
A BOY IN A RED SHIRT –
JUST DISAPPEARED
– GONE –
– JUST LIKE THAT –
WHERE THE HELL IS IT?
NOW WHAT AM I GOING TO TELL THE PARENTS?

GOOD RUN ASHORE?
YES, CAP'N. I GOT SERENA TO THE AUSTRALIAN PLACE.
WELL, YOU GOT THAT HALF RIGHT.
WHAT D'YOU MEAN?
!
BUT SHE WAS SUPPOSED TO –
DAMMIT!
WHAT ARE YOU DOING? I TOLD YOU TO STAY THERE!
MY PARENTS HAVE SEEN ME. THEY KNOW I'M ALIVE. AND YOU DIDN'T FINISH TELLING ME WHAT THIS IS ALL ABOUT.
D'YOU KNOW HOW INFURIATING THAT IS?
CAPTAIN, I –
STOW IT.
COME ON, FURL THESE SAILS! GET 'EM IN! JUMP TO IT!

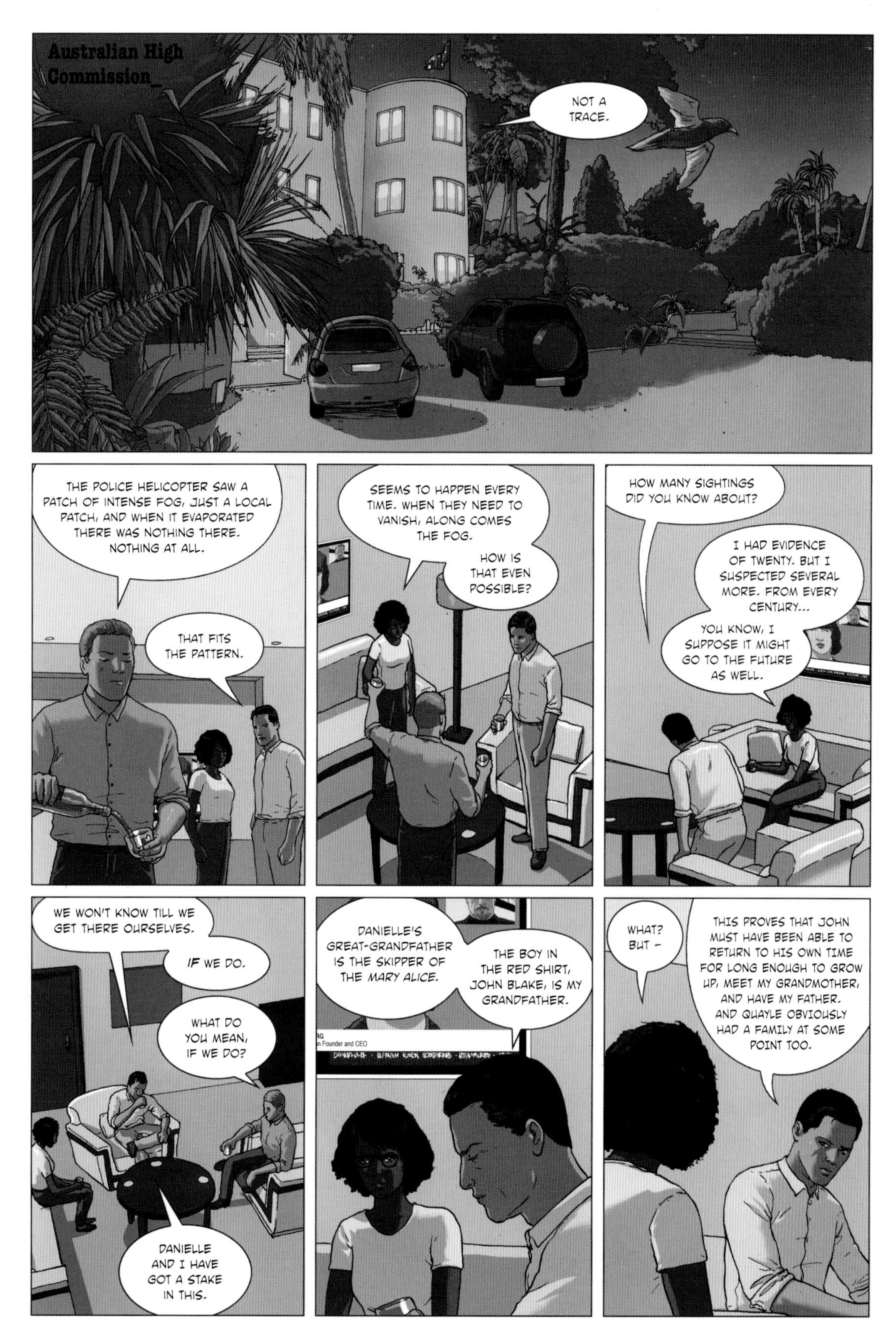
Australian High Commission_
NOT A TRACE.
THE POLICE HELICOPTER SAW A PATCH OF INTENSE FOG, JUST A LOCAL PATCH, AND WHEN IT EVAPORATED THERE WAS NOTHING THERE. NOTHING AT ALL.
THAT FITS THE PATTERN.
SEEMS TO HAPPEN EVERY TIME. WHEN THEY NEED TO VANISH, ALONG COMES THE FOG.
HOW IS THAT EVEN POSSIBLE?
HOW MANY SIGHTINGS DID YOU KNOW ABOUT?
I HAD EVIDENCE OF TWENTY. BUT I SUSPECTED SEVERAL MORE. FROM EVERY CENTURY...
YOU KNOW, I SUPPOSE IT MIGHT GO TO THE FUTURE AS WELL.
WE WON'T KNOW TILL WE GET THERE OURSELVES.
IF WE DO.
WHAT DO YOU MEAN, IF WE DO?
DANIELLE AND I HAVE GOT A STAKE IN THIS.
DANIELLE'S GREAT-GRANDFATHER IS THE SKIPPER OF THE *MARY ALICE*.
THE BOY IN THE RED SHIRT, JOHN BLAKE, IS MY GRANDFATHER.
WHAT? BUT –
THIS PROVES THAT JOHN MUST HAVE BEEN ABLE TO RETURN TO HIS OWN TIME FOR LONG ENOUGH TO GROW UP, MEET MY GRANDMOTHER, AND HAVE MY FATHER. AND QUAYLE OBVIOUSLY HAD A FAMILY AT SOME POINT TOO.

BUT DID YOU KNOW HIM WHEN YOU WERE A BOY? THIS IS AMAZING.
NO. I KNOW VERY LITTLE ABOUT HIM, EXCEPT THAT HE VANISHED – AGAIN – IN 1939.
SO DID THE SHIP! YOU DON'T THINK –
I DON'T KNOW WHAT I THINK, EXCEPT THIS: IF THEY'RE KILLED BEFORE THEY GET BACK INTO THEIR OWN TIME, THERE WON'T BE A ME, AND THERE WON'T BE A YOU.
SHEESH... I HADN'T THOUGHT OF THAT.
MY GOD.
AND WHO DO YOU THINK IS TRYING TO DO THAT? KILL 'EM I MEAN?
HIM.
APPARATOR SOLAR LAUNCH PARTY SET TO WOW GLOBE
CARLOS DAHLBERG!?! ARE YOU SURE?
I KNOW HE IS...
LIVE
APPARATOR SOLAR LAUNCH PARTY SET TO WOW GLOBE
NEWS
I JUST DON'T KNOW WHY.
LIVE
APPARATOR SOLAR LAUNCH PARTY SET
NEWS
SO HOW DO WE FIND OUT?
SAN FRANCISCO
PPARATOR SOLAR LAUNCH PARTY SET TO WOW GLOBE
NEWS
ANYONE FANCY GOING TO A PARTY?

WHAT ELSE CAN IT DO?
YOU CAN SEND STUFF, YOU KNOW, PICTURES, VIDEOS, FILES, WHATEVER YOU WANT. IT'S WATER-PROOF, AND, OH, THE BATTERY LASTS FOREVER.
LOST ME AGAIN.
OH YEAH. I KEEP FORGETTING THAT YOU GUYS ARE PALAEOLITHIC.
SERENA, YOU SAID THE COMPANY THAT MAKES IT IS CALLED THE DAHLBERG CORPORATION.
YEAH.
WHY?
BECAUSE...
... IT'S CARLOS DAHLBERG WHO'S BEEN TRYING TO KILL US.
WHY WOULD HE CARE ABOUT THE *MARY ALICE*? HE'S A GAZILLIONAIRE.
LISTEN: WE WERE IN SAN FRANCISCO IN 1973 –
YEAH, THE OLD MAN WENT LOOKING FOR HIS FAMILY HOUSE –
AND WE STAYED THERE FOR MORE TIME THAN USUAL – ABOUT A WEEK...

AND THERE WAS A STUDENT WHO USED TO HANG ABOUT THE WATERFRONT, AND WE GOT TALKING ONE DAY ABOUT PHYSICS AND ELECTRONICS...
KEVIN DANIELS, THAT WAS HIS NAME.
AND BECAUSE I KNEW A FEW THINGS, WE GOT FRIENDLY, AND HE TOLD ME HE'D INVENTED A NEW KIND OF BATTERY, BUT HE COULDN'T GET FUNDING TO DEVELOP IT – AND ALSO A THING CALLED AN OPERATING SYSTEM, MUCH BETTER THAN ANY OTHER THERE WAS.
HE HAD TO EXPLAIN WHAT THAT MEANT. IT WAS EXTRAORDINARY – AMAZING. IT WAS LIKE A REVELATION TO ME.
BUT HE HAD A RIVAL – ANOTHER STUDENT CALLED DAHLBERG, THAT'S RIGHT, CARLOS DAHLBERG. KEVIN WAS AFRAID THAT DAHLBERG WOULD STEAL HIS WORK BEFORE HE COULD PATENT IT.
AND THEN ONE NIGHT...
OPEN
Camille's DINER
KEVIN WAS GOING TO TAKE A BUS UP TO SEATTLE, SEE IF HE COULD GET SOME FUNDING. HE HAD HIS PROTOTYPE BATTERY AND THE WHAT DO YOU CALL THEM – TAPES, DISKS, SOMETHING, OF THE OPERATING SYSTEM IN HIS BACKPACK.
BEFORE HE WENT WE MET UP AND HE DREW AN OUTLINE OF THE OPERATING SYSTEM AND THE FORMULA FOR THE METAL HE USED IN THE BATTERY.
OPEN
Camille's DINER
LISTEN, JOHN – I'M GONNA LEAVE THESE NOTES WITH YOU, OK?
WHY?
WE'RE HOMEWARD BOUND TOMORROW
ONE MORE DAY
BECAUSE... JUST IN CASE. IF THAT DAHLBERG EVER –
BUT I'M NOT GOING TO BE HERE FOR LONG.
WHERE YOU GOING?
OH, ROCK AND ROLL ME OVER
ONE MORE DAY
IF I HAD LONG ENOUGH TO TELL YOU, YOU STILL WOULDN'T BELIEVE ME...
TAKE 'EM ANYWAY.
KIND OF INSURANCE.
DAY A-HOWLIN'
CAN'T YOU HEAR THE GALS A-CALLIN'
SIGN THEM FIRST. WRITE THE DATE TOO.
KIND OF INSURANCE.

DON'T YOU HEAR THE OLD MAN GROWLIN'
DON'T YOU HEAR THE MATE A HOWLIN'
DON'T YOU HEAR THE CAPS'N PAWLIN'
DON'T YOU HEAR THE PILOT BAWLIN'
ONLY ONE MORE DAY A-HOWLIN'
CAN'T YOU HEAR THE GALS A-CALLIN'
OPEN
ONLY ONE MORE DAY A-ROLLIN'
CAN'T YOU HEAR THE GULLS A-CALLIN'
!
HEY!
ONLY ONE MORE DAY A-FURLIN'
ONLY ONE MORE DAY A-CURSIN'
NO MORE GALES OR HEAVY WEATHER
KEVIN! WHAT THE –
ONLY ONE MORE DAY TOGETHER
YAARGH!
OPEN
DINER

!
SO DAHLBERG STOLE THE OPERATING SYSTEM? AND THE BATTERY IDEA? THEY MADE HIM FAMOUS! THEY MADE HIM THE RICHEST MAN IN THE WORLD!
WELL, HE KNOWS THAT I KNOW HE STOLE IT, AND THAT HE KILLED THE MAN WHO DID INVENT THEM.
THAT'S INCREDIBLE... BUT HOW COULD YOU PROVE IT?
HE'S LIKE... UNTOUCHABLE.
THE INSURANCE POLICY I MENTIONED.
PHOTOGRAPHIC EVIDENCE.
PLUS THE ORIGINAL NOTES, SIGNED BY KEVIN.
...
AND THAT'S KEVIN... DEAD?
AND DAHLBERG CAUGHT IN THE ACT.

WOW.
AND YOU'VE JUST HAD THE FILM HERE ALL ALONG?
YOU NEVER KNOW WHEN YOU MIGHT NEED SOMETHING.
KEEP THEM. WHEN YOU GET HOME YOU CAN BRING DOWN THE EMPIRE OF CARLOS DAHLBERG.
SO WHAT DO WE DO NOW?
YOU DO NOTHING. WE GET YOU BACK TO YOUR PARENTS WHERE YOU BELONG.
BU-
NO 'BUTS', CAPTAIN'S WORD IS FINAL.
JOHN, YOU'RE UP. LET'S SEE IF WE CAN REUNITE OUR LATEST CREW MEMBER WITH HER FAMILY.
I'LL TRY, CAPTAIN.
THAT'S ALL ANYONE CAN ASK.
NOW, JUMP TO IT!

WELL, MARY ALICE, WE'RE IN FOR A FIGHT. THAT MAN DAHLBERG WANTS TO KILL ME, NO QUESTION. HE'S THE RICHEST MAN IN THE WORLD – IT WON'T BE EASY TO FIGHT HIM.
AND THE WATCH... THE MECHANISM IN MY MIND. THERE'S A PIECE MISSING.
I CAN SORT OF SEE THE SHAPE, BUT –
?!
WHAT ARE YOU DOING?
WHO ARE YOU TALKING TO?
I'M TALKING TO MARY ALICE, AND IT'S A PRIVATE CONVERSATION.
SHE LOOKS FRIENDLY. SHE WOULDN'T MIND ME LISTENING.
SHE'S THE SPIRIT OF THE SHIP. YOU MIND YOUR MANNERS. AND KEEP STILL.
HOW'S IT WORK?
WHAT?
THE WATCH. THAT'S HOW YOU DO IT ISN'T IT?
DO WHAT?
THE FOG, THE JUMPING THROUGH TIME. I KNOW IT'S YOU. IT'S OBVIOUS. SO COME ON, TELL ME.
IT'S ONLY ONE PIECE OF THE PUZZLE. JUST A NORMAL WATCH.
SEE?
AS TO YOUR QUESTION, I DON'T KNOW. THAT'S THE PROBLEM.
YOU SAID THERE WAS A SHAPE MISSING...
IN MY MIND. THE MACHINE MY FATHER WAS MAKING...
IT WAS TO DO WITH HOW SPACE AND TIME ARE CONNECTED. IF I COULD SEE IT AGAIN, I COULD GET US HOME.
I KEEP TRYING, I THINK OF PLACES. THE FOG COMES.
BUT I DON'T KNOW WHERE WE'LL END UP. I THINK MARY ALICE DOES THOUGH.

SHE'S JUST A SHIP!
IS SHE? MAYBE THE WOOD REMEMBERS THINGS WE DON'T. WE SEEM TO END UP WHERE WE NEED TO BE MORE TIMES THAN NOT.
BUT NOT WHERE YOU WANT TO BE. BACK HOME.
NO.
I DIDN'T MEAN TO...
IT'S OK.
WHAT IS THAT?
IT'S THE SEA-SERPENT. WE SAW IT ONCE IN THE SOUTH ATLANTIC.
IS THAT WHERE WE ARE NOW?
WE COULD BE ANYWHERE ... ANYTIME.
KARK! KARK!

KARK! KARK!
FLAY 'IM ALIVE!
FLAY 'IM ALIVE!
WHAT'S THAT?
BILLY BONES'S RAVEN...
CAP'N BONES'S SHIP IS THE ONLY ONE I EVER SAW FOLLOWED BY RAVENS. THEY CHASED THE GULLS AWAY.
SSSHH...
NON, NON, JE VOUS SUPPLIE!
JÉSUS CHRIST, PROTÉGEZ-MOI! PROTÉGEZ-MOI!
AAAIIIEEEAAAAGGGHHHH!
DO AS THE BIRD SAYS, YE SWABS! SLICE HIS UGLY SKIN OFF!
JOHN, WHAT'S HAPPENING?
SHHH...
ooOoOOOOooOOOMMMMMMMMMM..MMMMMM
WHAT IS IT?

IT'S BEAUTIFUL...
YOU EVER HEAR THE STORY OF ODYSSEUS AND THE SIRENS?
COVER YOUR EARS...

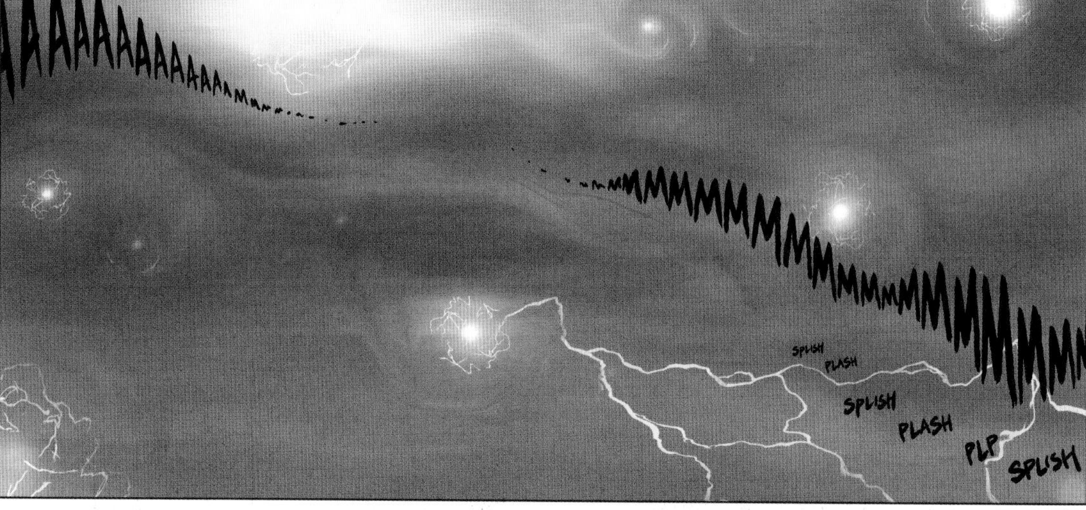
SPLISH
PLASH
SPLISH
PLASH
PLP
SPLISH

IT'S STOPPED BUT IT WAS SO BEAUTIFUL...
OH, I WANT TO HEAR MORE OF IT... I CAN'T BELIEVE HOW MUCH I WANTED TO JUST... GO TO THEM...
WE HEARD THEM ONCE BEFORE, AND LOST TWO CREWMEN. THEY JUST JUMPED OVERBOARD AND WE NEVER SAW THEM AGAIN.

LISTEN –

THIS IS THE SOUND OF THE FOG...
OOOoeeeeeeeeeiiiiiiii
...SSSSSSSssMMMMMMMGGRRROOO
THESE ARE ALL POSSIBILITIES.
SHHAAAASSHH
AAAAANNNNNNNNNNN...MMMMMMMM
KRAK!!!
ALL HERE AT THE SAME TIME...
AAHHHHHH...SSSSSSSSSSSSS
THE FUTURE...
THE PAST...
...FAREWELL AND ADIEU TO YOU, SPANISH LADIES
FAREWELL AND ADIEU TO YOU, LADIES OF SPAIN...
THINGS *DISSOLVE* IN THE FOG...
AAAAAAAAAAAAA
WE'RE HOMEWARD BOUND TOMORROW
ONE MORE DAY
!
HEAR THAT?
THAT SONG? I DON'T RECOGNISE IT.
OH, ROCK AND ROLL ME OVER
ONE MORE DAY
ONLY ONE MORE DAY A-HOWLIN'
CAN'T YOU HEAR THE GALS A-CALLIN'
DON'T YOU HEAR THE OLD MAN GROWLIN'
DON'T YOU HEAR THE MATE A HOWLIN'
SAN FRANCISCO. THAT'S IT.
THAT'S WHERE WE'RE GOING.

Flight from Fiji to San Francisco_
WHAT ON EARTH IS THAT?
I DON'T KNOW. I THINK IT HAS SOMETHING TO DO WITH OUR TIME-TRAVELLING RELATIVES.
IT'S HURTING MY BRAIN.
PLEASE PUT IT AWAY.
IT SEEMS TO HAVE THAT EFFECT ON PEOPLE.
...
IT'S A SCARY THOUGHT, YOU KNOW.
WHAT IS?
NOT EXISTING.

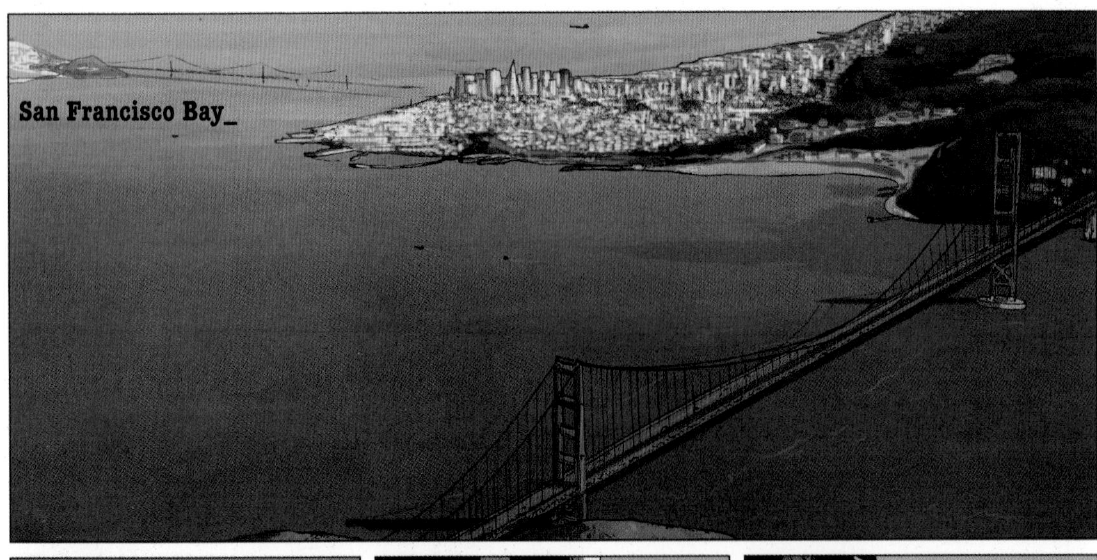
San Francisco Bay_

YES, THAT'S DEFINITELY DAHLBERG'S SHIP.

THERE ARE SO MANY ENTRANCES, I'M SURE I CAN FIND SOME WAY TO GET ABOARD.
OH?
EXPERIENCED STOWAWAY ARE YOU?
NOT INEXPERIENCED.
IT'S A QUESTION OF HOW MUCH ATTENTION THEY'RE PAYING –

ER – COMMANDER BLAKE? MS QUAYLE REID?
YES?
MY NAME IS BILL WILSON. I'M CARLOS DAHLBERG'S TECHNICAL CHIEF OF STAFF.
DID DAHLBERG SEND YOU?
NO. HE DOESN'T KNOW. THIS IS, UHH, IMPORTANT. MAY I?
WAIT A MINUTE. WHAT DO YOU WANT?
I GUESS YOU MIGHT BE THINKING OF GETTING ABOARD THE *SUPREMACY*.
GO ON.
YOU KNOW ABOUT THE LAUNCH PARTY TONIGHT? THREE HUNDRED GUESTS. THEY'RE BEGINNING TO ARRIVE ALREADY. AT NINE O'CLOCK THEY'RE GOING TO START CRUISING ROUND THE BAY TILL MORNING –
TELL ME ABOUT SECURITY.
AS WELL AS HIS NORMAL SECURITY STAFF THERE ARE TWENTY-FOUR GUARDS, EX-MARINES, UNDER THE COMMAND OF HENRY HARLAND. THEY'LL ALL BE ON DUTY TONIGHT.
WHO WATCHES THE FACE RECOGNITION PROGRAM?
I DO.
AS SOON AS I SAW YOU ON IT, I CAME OUT TO FIND YOU. I'VE CHANGED SOME OF THE DETAILS; YOU WON'T BE SPOTTED AGAIN.
I HAVE TWO GUEST PASSES FOR THE PARTY.
WHY ARE YOU DOING THIS?
BECAUSE HE'S INSANE. I THOUGHT IT WAS A RICH MAN'S OBSESSION BUT IT'S MORE THAN THAT. HE'S GOT DEATHWATCH MISSILES.
FOR HEAVEN'S SAKE, HE CALLS THEM HIS "SPECIAL GUESTS". I DIDN'T KNOW WHAT TO DO...

THERE ARE THREE TENDER DOCKS, A DOCK FOR THE SUBMARINE, AND TWO JET SKI DOCKS. IS THAT RIGHT?
YEAH, THAT'S IT.
WE'LL ARRIVE AT THE TENDER DOCK ON THE PORT SIDE AT NINE-THIRTY. CAN YOU MAKE SURE IT'S OPEN FOR BUSINESS?
SURE, ABSOLUTELY.
WE KNOW NOTHING ABOUT YOU. YOU COULD BE SETTING A TRAP.
IF YOU DON'T TRUST ME THEN I SUGGEST YOU GET AS FAR AWAY FROM HERE AS POSSIBLE. THAT'S WHAT I'M GOING TO DO.
YOU'RE LEAVING?
YEAH. I SIGNED UP FOR CORPORATE GREED NOT MISSILES, WORLD DOMINATION AND MASS MURDER.
DO YOU TRUST HIM? REALLY?
NOT REALLY, BUT THIS IS WHERE WE HAVE TO START TAKING RISKS.
LET'S GO AND RENT A BOAT.
Mary Alice
AREN'T HER FOLKS IN FIJI?
THIS DON'T LOOK LIKE FIJI.
SEEMS OUR DEAR MARY ALICE HAS OTHER PLANS.

ACH! WHAT'S THAT?
THAT'S CARLOS DAHLBERG'S YACHT. IT SAYS THEY'RE HAVING A PARTY TO LAUNCH THE NEW APPARATOR TONIGHT.
VERY HUGLY SHIP.
HUGLY AS HELL. WE'LL SEE FOR OURSELVES SOON.
CAPTAIN! HOW ABOUT THIS?
"MARIN COUNTY HISTORIC VESSEL MUSEUM". WE COULD PARK THERE AND –
PARK!?
SORRY. YOU KNOW WHAT I MEAN. THEN THEY WOULDN'T NOTICE US.
IF WE DON'T DEAL WITH THIS NOW, CAPTAIN, WE MIGHT NEVER GET ANOTHER CHANCE.
I KNOW, JOHN.
I KNOW.

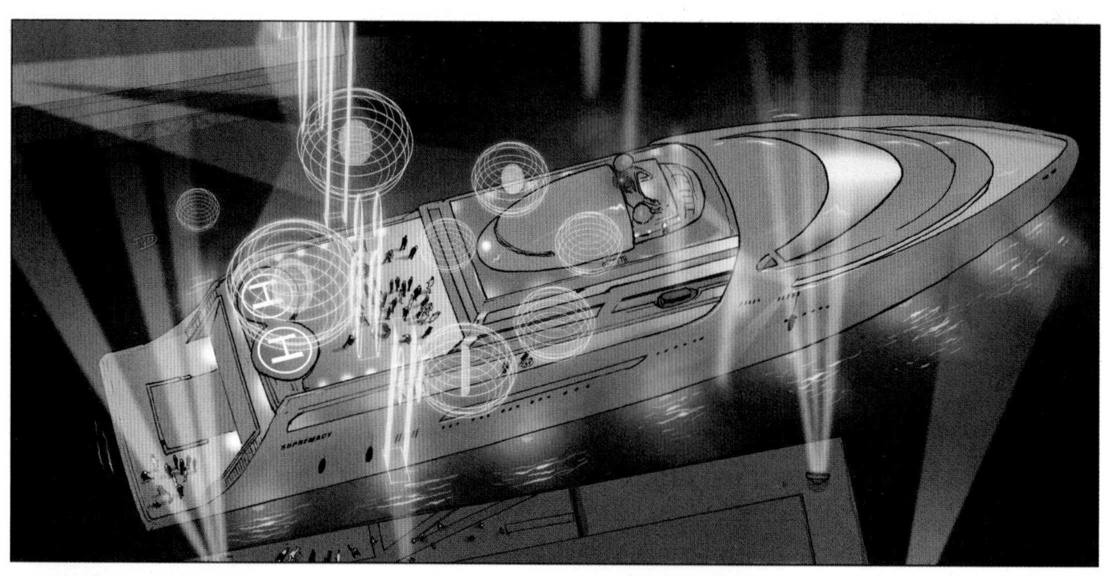

THE APPARATOR SOLAR IS THE MOST ADVANCED SMART DEVICE IN THE WORLD.

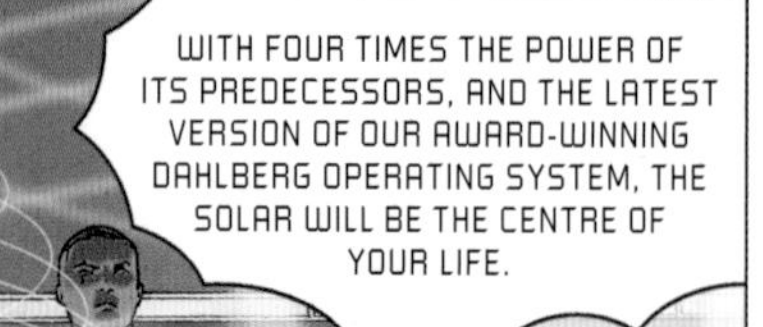
WITH FOUR TIMES THE POWER OF ITS PREDECESSORS, AND THE LATEST VERSION OF OUR AWARD-WINNING DAHLBERG OPERATING SYSTEM, THE SOLAR WILL BE THE CENTRE OF YOUR LIFE.
BOOP BOOP BOOP

YES?
SIR, WE'VE GOT SOMETHING.
IT HAD BETTER BE GOOD.
APPARATOR 45378GAMMA REGISTERED TO SERENA HENDERSON HAS JUST SYNCED WITH THE NETWORK.
AND WHERE ARE THEY?
THEY'RE RIGHT HERE, SIR.
IN SAN FRANCISCO BAY.

solar
solar

THERE SHE IS.
WE NEED THAT BOY IN ONE PIECE IF WE'RE TO GET WHAT WE WANT.
LET ME GO AND TALK TO THEM.
BRING HIM TO ME – AND MAKE SURE HE'S WEARING HIS WATCH.
BE READY.

DESERTED. LOOKS LIKE BILL CAME THROUGH.
JUST KEEP CRUISING AROUND. IF I NEED YOU, I'LL WHISTLE.
OH, YOU'LL JUST 'PUT YOUR LIPS TOGETHER AND BLOW'?
AND WHAT ELSE ARE YOU GOING TO DO IN THERE?
BREAK THINGS.

AHOY! *MARY ALICE*!
WHO ARE YOU AND WHAT DO YOU WANT?
NAME'S HARLAND, FROM THE *SUPREMACY*. I HAVE A MESSAGE FOR YOUR SKIPPER.
YONDER'S THE LADDER.
THIS WAY, MR HARLAND.
MR HARLAND FROM THE, UH - *SUPREMACY* TO SEE YOU, CAP'N.
SEND HIM IN, DAVY.

WELCOME ABOARD, MR HARLAND. TAKE A CHAIR.
CAPTAIN.
WHAT CAN I DO FOR YOU?
YOU CAN HAND OVER THAT BOY.
THE BOY HAS A NAME.
JOHN BLAKE.
WHY D'YOU WANT HIM?
HE'S A MURDERER.
HE STABBED TO DEATH A YOUNG MAN BY THE NAME OF KEVIN DANIELS IN SAN FRANCISCO IN 1973.
IT'S GOING TO BE HARD TO CONVINCE A JURY ABOUT THAT.
WHAT ARE YOU DOING, CAPTAIN?
SAILING AROUND IN A BUSTED OLD SCHOONER WITH A FREAK-SHOW CREW, DOLLING YOURSELVES UP IN FANCY DRESS TO SCARE OFF UNWANTED ATTENTION. AREN'T YOU TIRED OF IT ALL?
WE CAN HELP YOU. BUT I WANT THAT BOY.
IS THAT RIGHT?
YOU HOLD NO CARDS HERE, CAPTAIN. YOU'RE HARBOURING A FUGITIVE – A MURDERER. AND YOU KIDNAPPED A YOUNG AUSTRALIAN GIRL. TWICE!
IF YOU DON'T GIVE ME WHAT I WANT, WELL...
... I BELIEVE YOU KNOW WHO I WORK FOR.
YOU'RE A REAL CHARMER, MR HARLAND, I'LL GIVE YOU THAT. YOU REALISE YOU'RE ABOARD MY SHIP?
HOW'S ABOUT I STICK YOU IN THE CARGO HOLD AND USE YOU TO SCARE AWAY OUR NEXT UNWANTED ATTENTION?

CUTE. IF I'M NOT BACK ON MY SHIP IN TEN MINUTES, YOURS GETS BLOWN FROM THE WATER. HAND OVER THE BOY AND NO ONE NEEDS TO GET HURT. THINK OF THE GIRL, CAPTAIN.
HER BLOOD WILL BE ON YOUR HANDS.
CAN YOU LIVE WITH THAT?
WELL, TAKING EVERY ASPECT OF THE CASE INTO CONSIDERATION, MR HARLAND...
YOU CAN GO TO HELL.
YOU'RE ASKING FOR TROUBLE.
WE'VE MET MORE TROUBLE THAN YOU COULD DREAM OF, AND WE'VE COME OUT THE OTHER SIDE.
AND THE RESULT IS THAT I LOVE MY CREW, MR HARLAND. I'M TRYING TO TELL YOU SOMETHING YOU HAVE NO CONCEPTION OF. I TRUST THEM WITH MY LIFE, AND I LOVE THAT BOY LIKE A SON.
SO GO BACK TO YOUR GROTESQUE PARODY OF A SHIP AND TELL THAT LYING THIEF AND MURDERER DAHLBERG THAT IF IT'S TROUBLE HE WANTS, HE'LL GET MORE THAN HE BARGAINED FOR FROM THE *MARY ALICE*.
GOOD NIGHT TO YOU, SIR.
THE NIGHT'S JUST BEGINNING, ***CAPTAIN.***

I WANT THE BOY ALIVE. KILL THE OTHERS. SINK THE SHIP.
WELL, WE'RE IN FOR A FIGHT. I WISH I COULD TELL YOU SOMETHING ELSE. BUT IF EVER A VESSEL WAS PREPARED FOR A FIGHT, THE *MARY ALICE* IS THAT VESSEL.
SERENA, YOU'LL OBLIGE ME PERSONALLY BY GOING BELOW AND STAYING THERE.
AS FOR THE REST OF YOU, YOU KNOW WHAT TO DO. FIGHT WELL.
ENGINE FOR'ARD!
solar
HERE THEY COME, CAP'N.

CAN'T SEE ANY CREW, SIR –
THIS IS THE HAUNTED SHIP, AIN'T IT?
STOW THAT. GET ABOARD.
WHAT THE... MY HANDS ARE STUCK!
THE RAIL'S BEEN GLUED!
UH-OH –
BBLLBB-HHLLPP-BBLLBB –
SARGE! UP THIS WAY!
LOOKS CLEAR.

WHERE ARE THEY?
CAN'T SEE ANYONE –
THEY DOWN BELOW?

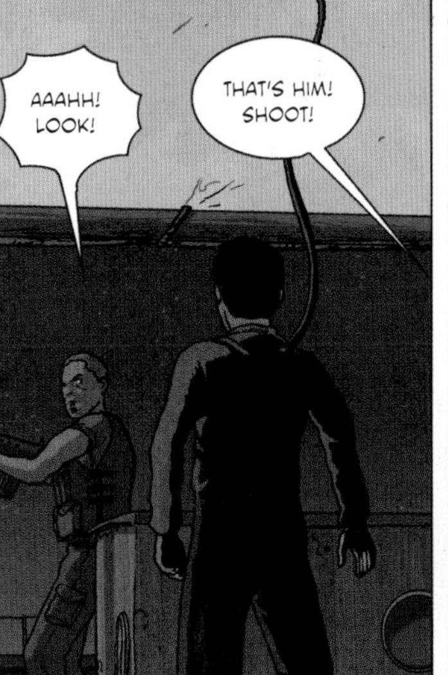
AAAHH! LOOK!
THAT'S HIM! SHOOT!

KRATATAT
PYANG
PING

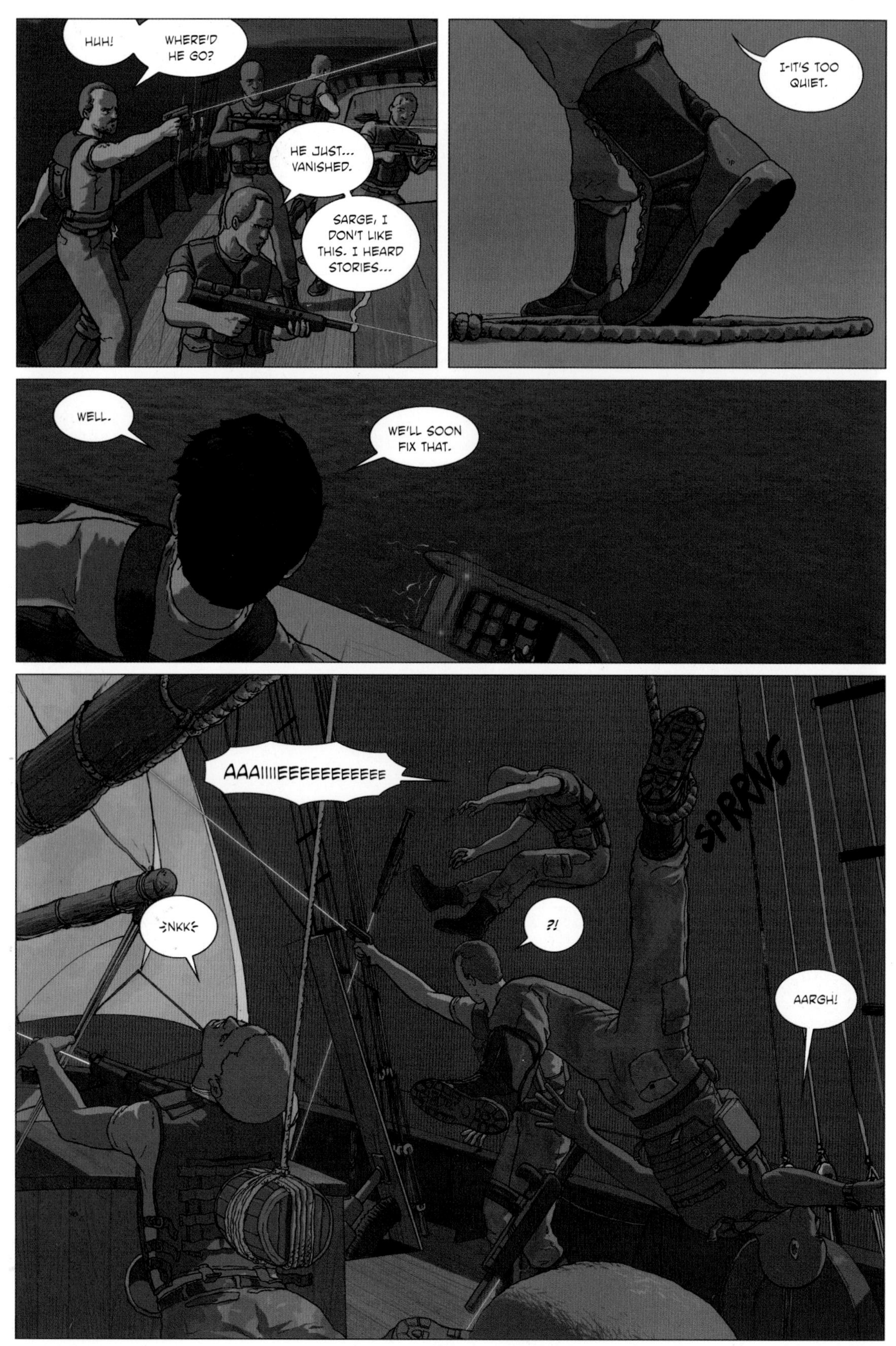
HUH!
WHERE'D HE GO?
HE JUST... VANISHED.
SARGE, I DON'T LIKE THIS. I HEARD STORIES...
I-IT'S TOO QUIET.
WELL.
WE'LL SOON FIX THAT.
AAAIIIIEEEEEEEEEEE
SPRRNG
?!
NKK
AARGH!

WHAT THE HELL?!

OPPRESSURUM!
WHAK
PANG
PING
SURPRISE!

TOK

SLAM!

THEY'RE SAILING STRAIGHT FOR US! AND WHERE ARE MY MEN? WHAT ARE THEY DOING?
SIR, THEY SEEM TO BE IN TROUBLE –
IMPOSSIBLE!
SUPREMACY
OH, GOD, WE'RE GONNA CRASH!

SERENA –
– GET DOWN TO THE ENGINE –
– PUT HER IN NEUTRAL –
THAT'S THE LAST OF 'EM!
BOARD, BOYS! BOARD!
HOLD IT!
HOLD IT RIGHT THERE.
THIS HERE'S A BLACK TIE FUNCTION, FELLAS. I'M GOING TO HAVE TO ESCORT YOU –
WAK!
HE HAS A POINT, YOU KNOW.
DIDN'T YOU READ YOUR INVITATION?

YOU GOOD GUY OR BAD GUY?
I'M WITH YOU AND THE *MARY ALICE*. YOU NEED TO GET AWAY FROM HERE. DAHLBERG HAS TURNED THIS MONSTROSITY INTO A WARSHIP AND HE WANTS YOU DEAD.
THE *MARY ALICE* DOESN'T RUN FROM A FIGHT.
THEN FOLLOW ME. BUT DON'T RUN.
PROVIDED WE WALK WITH SUFFICIENT CONFIDENCE, THESE HIGH SOCIETY TYPES'LL ASSUME YOU'RE PART OF THE SHOW.
HOW D'YOU KNOW WHO WE ARE?
I DON'T KNOW ALL OF YOU. YOUR NAME'S JOHN BLAKE, RIGHT?
YES. WHO ARE YOU?
MY NAME'S ROGER.
COMMANDER, ROYAL NAVY.
BUT –
MORE LATER.

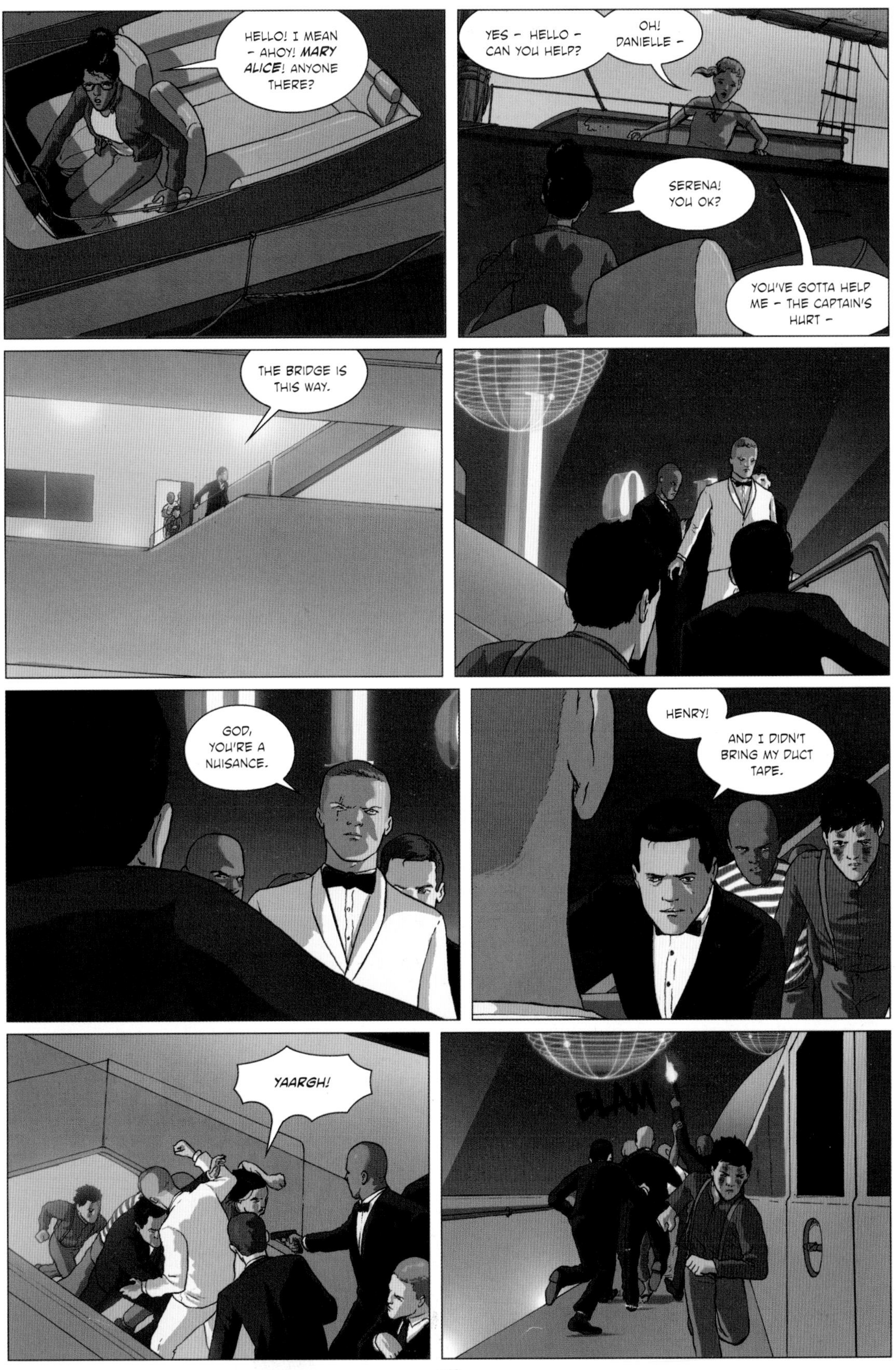
HELLO! I MEAN – AHOY! **MARY ALICE**! ANYONE THERE?
YES – HELLO – CAN YOU HELP?
OH! DANIELLE –
SERENA! YOU OK?
YOU'VE GOTTA HELP ME – THE CAPTAIN'S HURT –
THE BRIDGE IS THIS WAY.
GOD, YOU'RE A NUISANCE.
HENRY!
AND I DIDN'T BRING MY DUCT TAPE.
YAARGH!
BLAM

GET OUT.
NOW!
TIME FOR A COURSE CORRECTION.
STEP AWAY FROM THERE, BOY...

CARLOS DAHLBERG. I HAVEN'T SEEN YOU FOR FORTY YEARS.
YOU LITTLE PIECE OF SCUM.

HAND OVER THE WATCH.

YOU KNOW I WON'T DO THAT.
YES, YOU WILL.

DON'T BE SO SURE. YOU SEE, I'VE GOT A BONE TO PICK WITH YOU. THE SHIPMATES OF MINE THAT YOU KILLED –
MORE SCUM. THE SWEEPINGS OF THE SEVEN SEAS.
GOOD MEN, ALL OF THEM.
GUNNAR EYJOLFSSON, SHOT IN THE BACK OFF JAVA HEAD.
ARTURO CHAVEZ, DROWNED IN THE RED SEA – YOU COULDN'T FIND ME, SO YOU KILLED HIM.
ABDEL AZIZ, CUT TO PIECES BY YOUR CREW IN BAHÍA BLANCA BECAUSE HE WOULDN'T TELL YOU WHERE I WAS.
THEY'RE WITH ME NOW. YOU CAN'T SEE THEM?
SO MUCH THE WORSE FOR YOU –
RRAAARGHH!!
HA!
CLOSE!

KRAK
MIND YOUR BOAT, NOW, CARLOS!
I HAVE TO HAND IT TO YOU, BOY...
YOU'RE QUICKER ON YOUR FEET THAN YOUR OLD FRIEND KEVIN.
RARRL
NN
DOFF
YAARGH!

TIME TO SAY GOODBYE, JOHN BLAKE.

CLUNG-KNG
SCRRRREEEEEEEEEEEEEEEEE
AARGH

AAARGH! WHAT HAVE YOU DONE TO MY SHIP?
I'M VERY SORRY, HENRY...
BUT YOU'VE BECOME SURPLUS TO REQUIREMENTS.
AAAAHHHHHHHH
SPLOSH!

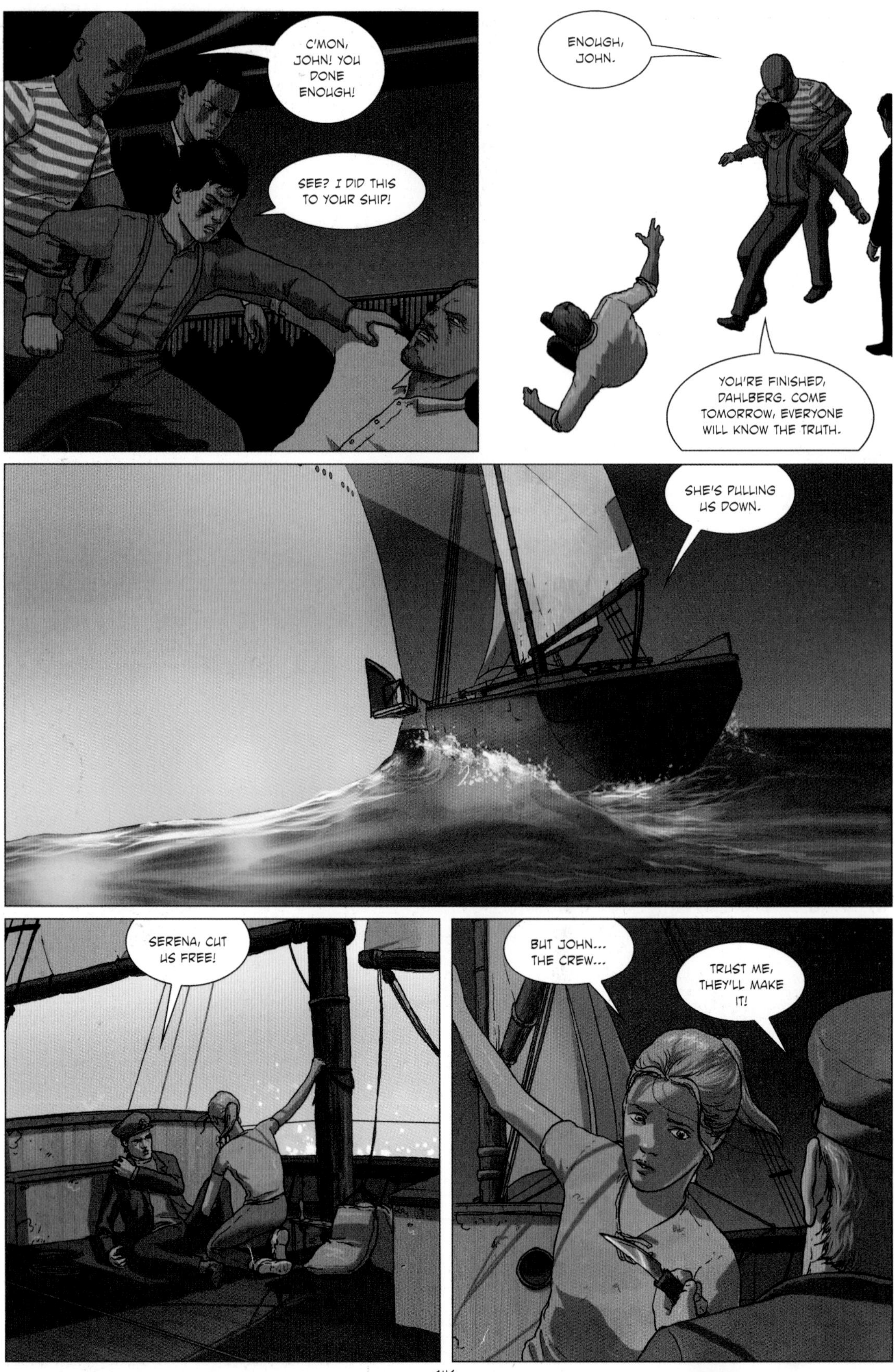
C'MON, JOHN! YOU DONE ENOUGH!
SEE? I DID THIS TO YOUR SHIP!
ENOUGH, JOHN.
YOU'RE FINISHED, DAHLBERG. COME TOMORROW, EVERYONE WILL KNOW THE TRUTH.
SHE'S PULLING US DOWN.
SERENA, CUT US FREE!
BUT JOHN... THE CREW...
TRUST ME, THEY'LL MAKE IT!

ENGINE!
FOR'ARD!
CLANG
SHNG
GNG
RRRMMM
BBBBB
solar

FWEEET
...BBBRRRM
GET IN! IT'LL TAKE US ALL, BUT GET IN!

THERE SHE IS!
JOHN!
SERENA! SERENA! YOU GOTTA COME NOW! COME ON!
SERENA! COME ON!
OK, I'M REALLY GOING THIS TIME.
GOODBYE, SERENA.

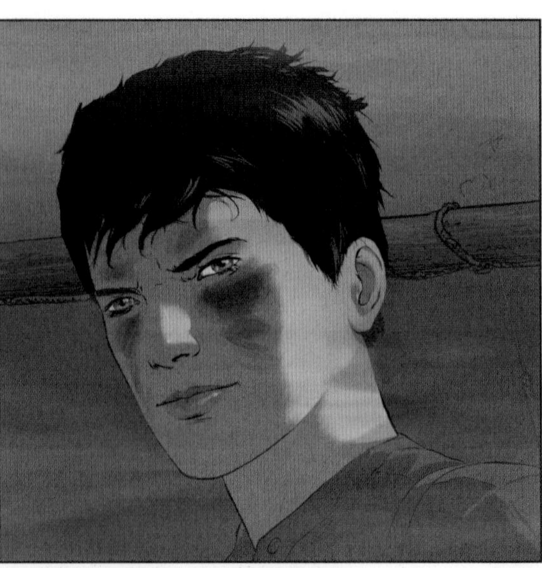

JOHN!
JOHN! *CATCH!*

...
THIS IS THE MISSING SHAPE...

WHO *ARE* YOU?
I'M YOUR *GRANDSON!*

TARGET LOCATED.
MISSILE SYSTEMS ONLINE.
WELL, JOHN, I MAY NOT HAVE DISCOVERED YOUR SECRET...

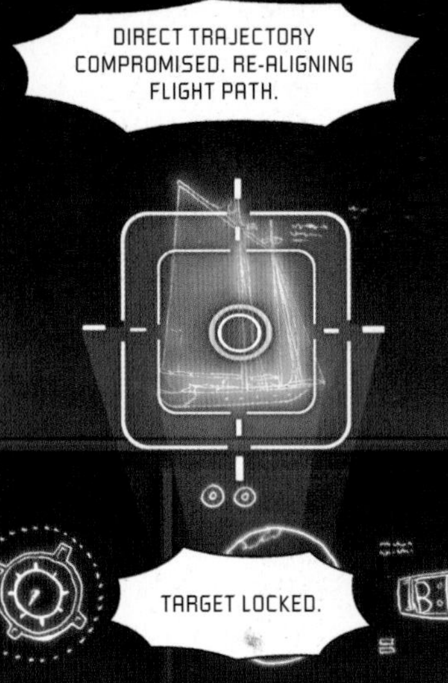
DIRECT TRAJECTORY COMPROMISED. RE-ALIGNING FLIGHT PATH.
TARGET LOCKED.

... BUT NO ONE'S GOING TO KNOW MINE EITHER.

SSSHAAAAASSHHHHH
WHAT THE HELL WAS THAT?
IT'S ARCING ROUND!
THEY'VE LAUNCHED A GODDAMN MISSILE!
JOHN, GET US OUTTA HERE!
JOHN!!

GOT IT.
FFFFWAAASSSSHHHHHHHHH

SUPREMACY
THOOM!

JEEZ!
WHAT ABOUT DAHLBERG?
I SAW THE AIR AMBULANCE LIFT HIM OFF. HE'LL BE AROUND FOR A WHILE YET.
BUT HE WON'T BE OUT AND ABOUT MUCH – THE AUTHORITIES TEND TO FROWN ON PRIVATE CITIZENS FIRING MISSILES TO SETTLE PERSONAL SCORES – HOWEVER RICH THEY ARE.
AND EVERY GUEST AT THAT PARTY WILL BE SUING HIM FOR A FORTUNE.
OH, I ALMOST FORGOT...
WHAT IS IT?
ANOTHER LITTLE SURPRISE FOR MR DAHLBERG...
FROM JOHN.
UPLOADING IMAGES TO GLOBAL NETWORK.
ISN'T SHARING A WONDERFUL THING?
HEY, DID YOU SAY YOU WERE JOHN'S *GRANDSON*?
THAT'S RIGHT.
WOW...
... HE MUST BE REALLY OLD.
WELL...

NOBODY'S
PERFECT.

THE ADVENTURES OF
JOHN BLAKE

THE CREW

CAPTAIN QUAYLE has a chequered and colourful past. A sailor and leader right down to his bones, Quayle is a man who finds the rolling waves of the ocean a comfort and dry land a prison. Though he has made many a promise to settle down, the call of the open sea has always proved too strong. Along the way he has been a husband, a father, a merchant, a navy man, a smuggler and everything in-between. Whatever he does he is firm, steady and resolute.

JOHN BLAKE'S father was involved in a top-secret weapons programme. He hitched a ride on Einstein's scientific voyage to test out one of his weapons experiments, taking John with him. But the experiment went horribly wrong. John was caught in the blast and thrown overboard. Luckily the *Mary Alice* was nearby. Quayle's crew hauled John from the sea, but it soon became clear that much more than just the bedraggled boy had come aboard. Strange energies soon engulfed the *Mary Alice* and her journey through time began.

SERENA HENDERSON is a schoolgirl from Sydney and is addicted to her Apparator. Her parents have taken her and her younger brother out of school for a year to sail around the world, which Serena thinks is pretty cool. It gets even more incredible when she finds herself a temporary member of the crew of the *Mary Alice*, travelling though space and time, after being washed overboard during an epic storm. John Blake rescues her and then begins the adventure of a lifetime!

SAMMY WU is from a wealthy family who made their fortune in the silk trade in the 1890s. But just as Sammy was set to take over the family business, a freak storm in the South China Sea left his junk wrecked. Sammy survived for a month – and fought off anything that wanted to eat him – before the *Mary Alice* hauled him to safety. While he enjoys the excitement that life aboard the *Mary Alice* offers him, he regrets missing out on the life of luxury that would have been his destiny.

DAVY JOHNSON was a deckhand on the original *Mary Alice* and has been a crew member throughout her travels through space and time. When the crew's original mate was lost overboard in the Arctic Ocean, Captain Quayle promoted Davy. He and the captain have an almost telepathic understanding of each other and have saved one another from death countless times. Of all the crew members, it's Davy who actually enjoys their strange situation the most.

MARCUS TULLIUS PALLAS served as an engineer in the legions of Emperor Septimus Severus. On returning to Rome, Marcus hung up his gladius and tried civilian life. But the call of the open road proved too strong and he set out for the northern borders of the Roman Empire. The crew of the *Mary Alice* rescued him from the amorous attentions of a Germanic warchief's daughter and once Marcus caught sight of the diesel engine he knew he'd found his true love.

CHARLIE BANKS grew up as an orphan on the streets of London and soon found himself in trouble with the law. Forced to choose between jail and the life of a sailor, he went to sea. In the summer of 1790 Charlie became a deckhand on HMS Bellerophon, but during a battle he fell overboard and floated, clinging to an empty rum barrel, for a day and a half before being rescued by the *Mary Alice*.

DICK MERRIFIELD was a simple fisherman from a village on the Devon coast. Happily married with two children, his life was torn apart by a Barbary pirate raid on his village. Dick was taken prisoner and to this day he doesn't know what happened to his family. A slave for the three years, Dick has a deep hatred of slavery and those who enslave others. After attempting to escape many times, his life was saved by the timely arrival of the *Mary Alice*.